THE ASSESSMENT OF
SCIENTIFIC SPECULATION

THE ASSESSMENT
OF
SCIENTIFIC SPECULATION

A survey of certain current views

R. A. R. Tricker, Ph.D.

NEW YORK

AMERICAN ELSEVIER PUBLISHING COMPANY, INC.

309087

U.S.A. Edition 1965

AMERICAN ELSEVIER PUBLISHING COMPANY, INC.

52 Vanderbilt Avenue,

New York 17, New York

LIBRARY OF CONGRESS CATALOG CARD NUMBER 65–19253

Printed in Great Britain by
William Clowes and Sons, Limited, London and Beccles

But it is always safe and philosophic to distinguish, as is in our power, fact from theory; and the experience of past ages is sufficient to show us the wisdom of such a course; and considering the constant tendency of the mind to rest on an assumption, and, when it answers every present purpose, to forget it is an assumption, we ought to remember that it, in such cases, becomes a prejudice, and inevitably interferes, more or less, with a clear-sighted judgment.

MICHAEL FARADAY

CONTENTS

PLATES

PREFACE

This book has its origin in an educational problem. Science enters today, as it should, into the education of all. Too often, however, what is done lacks intellectual value. The work is sometimes dull, amounting to little more than rote learning. As a vehicle for an education its role is very limited. What aims should be selected is a matter of attitude and this depends upon philosophy. This book is an attempt to illuminate the problems by means of a discussion of various views which are held today, of the philosophy of the subject.

The educational problem appears in its most acute form in the education of the "practical man". The generic term engineer might be applied to this class of person but it includes the medical profession, agriculturalists and chemists, in addition to mechanical and electrical engineers. They learn science in order to be able to apply it and are often brought up on a restricted diet of memorisation of principles learnt dogmatically and exercise in their application. Rarely are they called upon for any effort of criticism. Moreover, what are learnt as facts are, as often as not, views and theories and a completely wrong view of scientific achievement is conveyed. We need to get clear what kind of knowledge science is capable of providing and what students can be expected to "know" at the end of their course.

It is unnecessary to go outside the field of the practical man to substantiate a claim for something better. The practical man is interested in his theory in order to be able to apply it, but concepts can be applied out of context. If he is ever to be able to face a new situation, he, of all people, needs to know that the concepts he uses possess limitations and what they are.

Others who study science for the more general purposes of education are less difficult to convince of the necessity of a reasoned approach. Matthew Arnold's arguments for a general education were based upon the necessity for a man to know himself and the world in which he is placed. Science deals with man's physical environment. The researcher uses theories as tools for exploring that world, but while a man remains a student his main demand of a theory is that it should provide a convenient summary of existing knowledge. This remains the practical man's requirement throughout. Both student and researcher, however, need to be able to distinguish knowledge from hypothesis, the student in order to know what can properly be called knowledge and the researcher to realise how theoretical limits may be explored and extended.

This can only be achieved through a critical approach to the work and a study of what may be termed "evidence". It is through a failure to assemble evidence that the shortcomings mentioned above have arisen. The evidence required is not necessarily as to whether or not a theory is "true", which may be an unanswerable question, but simply evidence which shows that the theory works and delineates the field to which it can be applied. Most scientific concepts take over and embody more limited ones employed earlier and they cannot be studied properly in isolation from them. If an attempt is made to do so it inevitably results in the theories appearing gratuitous and extravagant. The newer ideas of the quantum theory of physics, for example, were but an extension of the classical theories, and, just as much as the mechanical models of the nineteenth century, they themselves are based upon mechanics.

The educational value of a subject depends upon an appreciation of its philosophy. Its philosophy furnishes a critique of its reasoning and determines the problems to which it can be applied, as well as the measure of success to be expected in dealing with them. Rarely can a philosophy achieve finality and it has certainly not been reached in the philosophy of science. Four views are discussed in this book. One or other of them is likely to be adopted according to the aims which are selected as appropriate for a scientific enquiry. From the point of view of the educational problem just raised, however, all indicate the same line of action. Without a reasoned study none of the purposes of science can be satisfactorily attained.

The author would like to record his special indebtedness to his former colleague, Mr G. F. Peaker, who not only read the first draft of the book and made many valuable comments upon it, but also first put the author in touch with the particular demonstrations of Bayes' theorem and the Rule of Succession reproduced here and, further, called his attention to the work of Sir Harold Jeffreys. Mr Peaker would, no doubt, disagree with some of the conclusions reached in the book and the author takes full responsibility for them, but the discussions he had with him were of the greatest benefit in arriving at them. The author has also benefited from a large number of other authors. There is nothing particularly new in this book and the sources from which views have been assembled are indicated in the bibliography at the end of the book.

I am grateful to the Cambridge University Press for permission to quote from *Dilemmas* by Gilbert Ryle, to the Franklin Institute for permission to quote from the address by Lord Rutherford on the occasion of their centenary celebrations, to Messrs Hutchinson for permission to quote from *The Logic of Scientific Discovery* by Karl Popper, to Messrs Methuen for permission to quote from *Space and Sight* by M. von Senden, to The Open Court Publishing Company of La Salle, Illinois, for permission to quote from *The Philosophy of G. E. Moore*, and to the American Journal of Psychology for permission to reproduce the figure of the Invisible Man from Mr. H. B. Porter's article.

Part I

Chapter I

SCIENCE AND PHILOSOPHY

When the man who is interested in science, whether he would call himself a scientist or not, turns to philosophy to enquire what is the basis on which the subject rests and what is the reliability of the conclusions at which it arrives, he is apt to find the situation confusing. He may, perhaps, have felt that some of the statements which scientists make appear to outstrip the evidence available and may wish to enquire what credence he can reasonably give to them. In science itself he will have already found a readiness to admit to a degree of uncertainty, but just how uncertain its statements are, is rarely examined in detail. Nevertheless, at any given time, he will have noticed a wide general agreement among scientists on what the body of scientific knowledge comprises, although this is subject to revision from time to time. In philosophy, on the other hand, no such agreement exists. Views put forward by one author are contradicted by another and yet both continue to find supporters. Dead men fail to lie down—or perhaps it is that philosophic bullets are rarely fatal. Thus towards the beginning of the era of modern science he will find views about the world and possible knowledge of it put forward by Locke, in much the same form as is commonly accepted by science, only to be followed by Berkeley and Hume, who questioned the foundations on which these rest. Their objections have never been successfully answered, in spite of which science proceeds on its way apparently unconcerned by the controversy. Indeed among philosophers themselves he finds at a later date men like J. S. Mill on the one hand and Whewell and Jevons on the other continuing the discussion of what the scientific method amounts to and putting forward more or less opposing views on the matter. There are the claims of empiricism, logical atomism, linguistic analysis, positivism and operationalism. Some of these views are in conflict with or give an incomplete account of the procedure adopted by scientists in practice. Confronted by such a welter of opinions many find philosophy of little help, pursue the matter no further and simply relapse into the state of carelessness and inattention recommended by Hume.

It is not, however, good to forget the questions which philosophy asks. The certain knowledge which is available to us is very little and

3

to imagine that we have found the answers to them may well be worse. The diverse views on the nature of knowledge which have been expressed have arisen from the diversity of questions which have been asked, and the range of initial assumptions which have appeared acceptable to different schools as a basis from which to begin the argument. To Hume is due the demonstration that if we are not prepared to make any assumptions at all, then we are completely helpless. Reason is valueless and ordered activity impossible. If we are to live our lives at all, some basic assumptions have to be acted upon. The nature of the philosophy at which we arrive will depend upon just what these presuppositions are. On the whole, questions have turned out to be much more numerous than the answers which have been found. One of the principal functions of philosophy is to face doubts to which the intellect is subject and these are of obvious importance to anyone concerned to form for himself some sort of assessment of the doctrines of science. These doctrines are not fairy tales and are more or less closely connected with repeatable experience, the caveat "more or less" being necessary because the closeness of the connection varies greatly across the field of science. If these differences are to be recognised, and it is clearly important that they should be, then it follows that critical questions must be asked.

Philosophy must, therefore, to a certain extent be a personal thing depending upon the questions to which we attach particular importance. Whether or not we find answers it is nevertheless well to attempt to explore the repercussions upon the extent of natural knowledge we may expect to acquire, which the questions entail. Many, if not most of the questions we may wish to put will have been asked before in earlier contexts. It is the purpose of this book to survey and comment upon some of those questions and suggestions which have already been adumbrated. The space to be devoted to each topic can only be decided more or less arbitrarily. A good deal will be given to theories which depend upon considerations of probability, in spite of the fact that the general tendency today seems to be to turn in other directions for solutions to the problems of science. These theories have received their share of criticism, not all of which has been well founded. There are undoubtedly certain cases in which they can be shown to work. Whether the cases which the theory fits are sufficiently analogous to scientific problems in general for it to be used as a guide in the elucidation of the wider field is, perhaps, open to discussion, but it would appear to offer the only possible line of approach to the view which most scientists appear to adopt, that science does, in fact, uncover the inner nature of matter, and for this reason if for no other it demands consideration.

There are, broadly speaking, two views of the purpose of science. The first concerns science looked upon as a corpus of knowledge. The question which here demands an answer is how far the theories of science can be regarded as constituting knowledge of the world of nature. This is the view which has been questioned most frequently in the past and lies behind a great deal of philosophical thinking about the methods of science. To some, however, this view seems impossible to confirm and to them the main interest in scientific theories lies in their use for further exploration and discovery. To raise the question of how scientific theories may lead to further discoveries, however, leads to a rather different view of the philosophy of the subject. The fact is, of course, that a scientific theory has a dual role to play. On the one hand it has to serve as a convenient summary of results already obtained, and, on the other, as an indicator for further exploration. To serve as a summary of existing knowledge a theory has to be stripped of all its hypothetical elements. If this is not done there will be inevitable confusion as to what is and what is not known. It is from this point of view that have arisen the various brands of positivism and operationalism. But a theory stripped of its hypothetical content becomes useless as a tool for research. The two roles which a scientific theory has to fulfil are thus incompatible, and this has led to some confusion. It is in the ability to recognise the hypothetical content of a theory and thus to know what can be changed in it with little difficulty, that the mark of the scientist lies. It is precisely the difficulty of accomplishing this that besets the popularisation of science. In popular writings the theory is often considered apart from the experience upon which it is based, so that any critical evaluation becomes impossible, and for this reason a good deal of such writing about science makes little intellectual impact.

One of the major urges which led to the development of science is what Professor Popper has called the cosmological interest. "For myself," he says "I am interested in science and in philosophy only because I want to learn something about the riddle of the world in which we live and the riddle of man's knowledge of that world. And I believe that only a revival of interest in these riddles can save science and philosophy from narrow specialisation and from an obscurantist faith in the expert's special skill and in his personal knowledge and authority; a faith that so well fits our 'post-rationalist' and 'post-critical' age proudly dedicated to the destruction of the tradition of rational philosophy and of rational thought itself."

It has been such cosmological interest that has been the drive towards speculation since the time of the Greeks. The Greeks were very fruitful of ideas but did not develop the scientific method whereby

2

their ideas could be tested. It is largely to them that we owe the speculations concerning a hidden yet permanent world of reality lying behind the world of change which we experience directly. It was only by combining the speculation of the Greeks with a programme of testing that science was able to progress. The hidden world of reality, if it exists, can only be reached by means of hypothesis, and hypotheses can only be put to the test through an examination of their consequences. From the cosmological point of view the crucial question to which this gives rise is what reliance can be placed upon this combination of speculation and testing as providing knowledge of the world of reality.

To make a beginning we will accept this hypothetico-deductive view of the method of science. It raises a number of problems. There is to begin with how the hypotheses are to be fabricated in the first instance. This is important since they cannot be selected at random and the entire collection winnowed in order to extract the viable from the useless. The process is not only physically impossible but it is essential for a theory to start off with a finite probability of truth if it is ever to achieve acceptance. Then there is the process of testing—it is about this that most has so far been written—and finally there is the critical examination of what results. Each of these stages will be affected by the purposes we set before ourselves for the study of science. If we look to science to unravel the mystery of the universe, our attitude to the hypotheses, their testing and our final formulation of judgment will be different to that which we would adopt if we were looking merely for a tool with which we can explore the world of nature.

Chapter II

ON FRAMING HYPOTHESES

Most philosophies of science seem to start in the middle of the process. The first question is how may the initial hypotheses be found. This is rarely discussed. It is not by any means an easy one on which to get a line and, in consequence, most writers on the scientific method give most of their attention to the next stage which comes after. The bulk of what has been written deals with what is to happen when once the hypotheses have been adumbrated. Much has been said about how they may be tested and what the effects of the results of the tests may be upon the degree of credibility of the theories of which they form a part.

A view put forward by Whewell and Claude Bernard, and held fairly widely at the present time, is that which might be called the "hunch theory". The investigator seeking an explanation of certain phenomena has a "hunch" that they might be caused in a certain way. The view tells us very little about how hypotheses may be arrived at beyond perhaps indicating how very difficult it is to achieve an understanding of the process at all. To be able to have a hunch it is necessary to have adopted the attitude that a comprehensible explanation of the phenomenon exists and that existing experience is sufficient to enable it to be comprehended. The process whereby the hunch is obtained, however, still remains a mystery. Does it just happen or is there any process of ratiocination which is followed consciously or unconsciously, in arriving at the particular view of affairs which is being adopted? Is there anything which can be done to catalyse the development of the inspiration?

The hunch theory assumes the doctrine of causes and operates at the level of naive realism. In this chapter we shall not be concerned with difficulties which arise in deciding what a cause is or with questions of determinism or otherwise. We shall adopt the common sense view of the existence of the causally determined physical world assumed by the working scientist, and enquire how we might then decide what was the cause of something which has happened. Even so a variety of levels remains open to us.

A man has been found with a bullet in his brain and the cause of his death is sought by a court of enquiry. Such a court would not be in the least concerned with discussing the question of why the destruction of the man's brain led to his heart ceasing to beat, although his heart is operated by involuntary muscles not under the control of the brain. The investigation takes place at a quite different level and asks who fired the shot. Was it the man himself so that it was a case of suicide, or was the shot fired by somebody else and, if so, by whom? The fact that a bullet in the brain normally causes death would be taken for granted. In carrying out their investigation those concerned with the case would assemble all the evidence they felt to be relevant to these latter questions. In searching for evidence which was relevant they would be guided not only by common sense and everyday knowledge but also by possible theories about how the occurrence might have happened. Hypotheses would thus enter the field at an early stage and might, unless the examination was very carefully planned to avoid this source of error, colour the supposed facts of the case, only those emerging which happened to be suggested by the hypotheses which were being employed at the time.

Judicial enquiries are, as a rule, concerned with particular cases. Nevertheless the judicial procedure is, in essence, the same as that of science. Justice must be seen to be done; the available evidence must be marshalled and various possibilities tested against the facts thus established. It is true that while judicial conclusions rest upon a body of general experience it is the application of this general experience to a unique occurrence which is required. Science, on the other hand, usually deals with occurrences which can be repeated, though even in the case of science all that can be examined are particular instances. For repeatable events J. S. Mill enumerated a series of methods for arriving at the cause of a phenomenon. His methods appear obvious and common sense. They, or something very like them, probably underlie the process whereby the scientist arrives at his working hypotheses. Mill appears to have been of the opinion that they provided a solution to the problem of the method of science, but they do not take us as far as he thought. As far as the educational problem of designing a course in science is concerned, probably the most important conclusion to be reached is that the process of fabricating a hypothesis comes after a study of at least some part of the field with which it deals. There is no *deus ex machina* to start us off in the right direction. Some of the dullness of science courses arises because this simple fact is forgotten.

Mill's "method of agreement" is to notice what factor is common among a number of occurrences of the phenomenon. If all except one of the factors involved change without affecting the phenomenon itself, then the one common factor is either the cause or is related to the cause which is sought.

The method of agreement is a comparatively weak indicator of the cause. Francis Bacon tells a story which will serve to illustrate the uncertainty inherent in the method. It is of a man called Diagorus, who, in ancient times, was taken round a temple of Neptune and there shown, painted on the walls, portraits of those who had paid their vows to Neptune before setting out on a voyage by sea, and had subsequently made a successful voyage. On being asked, however, whether he was not thereby impressed by the necessity to pay vows to Neptune before making a sea voyage he replied "Aye, but where are they painted who paid their vows and were drowned?"

If only positive instances of the occurrence of a phenomenon are considered, then any concomitant factor, even though quite irrelevant, may be looked upon as the cause. Purveyors of patent medicines are never short of "unsolicited" testimonials, the writers of which have been misled in this way. The method is also the basis of unscrupulous special pleading; only evidence which supports the view the speaker wishes to have accepted is put forward, any contrary evidence being suppressed. The procedure is the exact opposite of anything which deserves to be called scientific. Scientific writers are quite properly concerned to show how certain facts may be accounted for on the basis of a theory. Difficult facts are often left to the reader to raise. It is assumed that the reader will be a specialist in the subject and will be thoroughly familiar with them. Unfortunately the same line is often taken by the writers of text-books so that the student is overwhelmed by a mass of positive instances, and hence is likely to be tempted to assume that recalcitrant facts do not exist.

Often the recalcitrant facts do not obtrude themselves and are most difficult to detect. In the age of blood-letting the practice of medicine was founded upon the necessity for the relief of "tensions" in the body. The aim of any therapy should be to secure relaxation. In pursuit of this end blood-letting was, in the hands of some practitioners, carried to heroic lengths, patients being nearly bled to death. When they reached the stage of syncope and fainted from loss of blood, relaxation was certainly achieved! Yet a proportion of them recovered and could be pointed to as evidence for the essential correctness of the treatment. Failures could be explained away on the basis that the treatment had not, in fact, been sufficiently severe. The position was impregnable.

When we attempt to form an opinion on the basis of a single example we often find ourselves in a similar situation. We catch a cold, try a new medicine and the cold disappears. What part did the medicine play in our recovery? If we are wise we suspend judgment until we have tried the remedy on other occasions. Perhaps the cold would have got better just as quickly had we done nothing about it. Even if we find that the medicine continues to "work" we cannot be very definite in our judgment until we have compared what happens when we again have a cold and do not take the remedy. This is the basis of Mill's "method of difference".

This method consists in noting the factors involved in a series of occurrences of a phenomenon and those involved in similar circumstances in which the phenomenon, as for example the cure of the cold, does not occur. If in all these cases there is one factor only which is always present when the phenomenon occurs but which is always absent when the phenomenon does not occur, then it is the cause or connected with the cause of the phenomenon.

The method of difference is clearly a much stronger method than that of agreement. It amounts to a search for a factor which, if present, is followed by the phenomenon but which if absent, is always followed by the absence of the phenomenon. We have not, so far, discussed what is meant by the term "cause" but for the moment this may, perhaps, serve as a definition of what the word "cause" is meant to imply. It is the word "always" in this definition which leads to difficulty.

In any scientific investigation it is desirable to vary one factor only at a time. It is then possible to see if its withdrawal leads to the disappearance of the phenomenon. If experiments are designed in which more factors than one are varied, the results become indecisive, although such experiments may be valuable in a preliminary way in narrowing down the possibilities. The methods of agreement and difference may be used jointly.

There are cases in which it is impossible to employ the method of difference, and when, in such cases, reliance has to be placed entirely on the method of agreement the evidence is much less decisive. It is often said that a theory has to "stick its neck out". That is to say, it must lead to forecasts which are capable of being disproved by observation. If the theory does not do this it becomes impossible to test it and it is doubtful if the term "scientific" is then appropriate to it at all. An example of this which will be elaborated in a later chapter is the atomic theory of matter. If this theory is to be subjected to thorough test it must furnish predictions which are capable of being falsified. But it is quite impossible to conceive of any phenomenon which is incapable of being explained on the basis of an atomic theory. The theory, in other words, is capable of accounting for whatever phenomena may be found. It thus becomes impossible to falsify it. As Dr Mary Hesse* says concerning Locke's discussion of the continuity and correspondence between the macroscopic and the microscopic, "... we are so accustomed to presupposing the seventeenth century world model according to which all physical

* *Forces and Fields*, page 125.

change is *really* produced by matter in motion, that we forget that this is in a sense a metaphysic; derived from the Greek metaphysical theory of atomism; established by the overthrow of opposing metaphysical systems, namely the Aristotelean, Stoic, and Neo-Platonic; and justified by the Pythagoreanism of Copernicus, Kepler and Galileo, and by the metaphysical arguments about primary qualities of Descartes, Galileo and Locke."

There are two ways in which this difficulty may be, at least partially, surmounted. The first is to treat atomic theories simply as a point of view—that is, as a way of regarding matter, irrespective of its ultimate truth or falsity. Such an attitude of detachment has much to commend it although those who are anxious to know the "truth" may find it unattractive. The second method is to regard the atomic theory as established by the falsification of its rival, namely the view that matter is a continuum. But if we are as ready to ascribe properties to the matter of the continuum as we have been accustomed to define the properties of the atoms, it is not clear, without much further consideration, that a theory of a continuum can be so easily disposed of. For example, we are accustomed to endow atoms with the property of combining together in simple fixed ratios. There is, however, not the slightest reason, *a priori*, why they should do so. We have simply transferred the properties of matter in bulk directly to the atoms of which we considered it to be composed. We could equally well have left the property attached to matter in bulk. This line of thought would tend to support the view of the atomic theory as a convenient mental picture since for many purposes, at least, it is undoubtedly easier to think in terms of atoms than of a continuum.

Other examples of an element of metaphysics contributing to the acceptance of scientific ideas now currently held, come readily to mind. One would be the principle of the conservation of energy. A good deal of more or less qualitative evidence accumulated during the seventeenth and eighteenth centuries in connection with experiments on perpetual motion machines, of which Bishop Wilkins, an early member of the Royal Society, was a pioneer. Later evidence from the well-known quantitative experiments on the heat equivalent of work was added, but the absence of any determination of the work equivalent of heat shows that the acceptance of the principle depended as much upon the combination of the occurrence of the conservation of energy in the Newtonian mechanics of a particle with the metaphysical conviction that everything is capable of being explained on the basis of the motion of Newtonian particles.

A similar example is provided by the Special Theory of Relativity. Experiments on the motion of charged particles left little doubt that they obeyed the Lorentzian equations of motion,

$$\frac{d}{dt}\left(\frac{m\dot{x}}{\sqrt{1-\frac{v^2}{c^2}}}\right) = F$$

rather than the Newtonian,

$$m\frac{d\dot{x}}{dt} = F$$

It was clear that electrodynamics stood in need of modification. The Michelson-Morley experiment is usually cited as the basis for Einstein's development of the theory of relativity but from this experiment his principle of the constancy of the velocity of light, on which the theory depends, cannot be deduced. The combination of the realisation of the need for change in electrodynamics with the metaphysical conviction that all matter is fundamentally electrical in nature, contributed largely to the acceptance which the theory was accorded. Predictions in the abstract mathematical theories of the fundamental particles appear to depend largely upon a Pythagorean belief that nature will necessarily follow some mathematical pattern and that a pattern which has been found to fit a limited number of cases will also fit new ones as they arise.

The last method of Mill which we need consider is that of "concomitant variation". If a phenomenon varies quantitatively in proportion as a particular factor is varied, then that factor may be looked upon as the cause or related to the cause of the phenomenon.

Although Mill appears to have considered that his methods were capable of giving much greater certainty than we would now be prepared to credit them with, there is, nevertheless, little doubt that they form an important ingredient in the thinking of many scientists. Even the rough method of agreement may be the initial pointer to a possible explanation which may then be examined more carefully. But to achieve certainty in this way it is necessary to be sure that all possible factors have been investigated and varied, and this it is hardly ever possible to secure. Even with the method of difference, when the force of the negative instance, which is always strongest, is employed, it may not be possible to ensure that in eliminating the factor which occupies the attention at the moment, some other factor may not have been eliminated simultaneously.

It is this difficulty of being able to enumerate completely all the factors involved in any case, which dogs many of the attempts which have been made to account for the use of the method of induction in scientific argument. Mill's methods have also comparatively little to do with the testing of a theory which has attained a high level of complexity. When, in such a case, disagreement with a theoretical prediction is obtained, it is from a whole nexus of interlocking ideas and hypotheses that experiment diverges, and it then often becomes a matter of choice which element of the theory should be modified to bring the whole into agreement with experience once more. Clear-cut tests of individual items in a complicated theory are often very difficult to design.

Chapter III

VERIFICATION

We come now to the central problem of the method of science. Assuming that the method consists in the formulation of hypotheses and the putting of these to the test of experiment, what is the effect of the successful passing of the tests? When the tests are passed successfully this is often spoken of as the verification of the hypothesis. Strictly speaking, however, it is not the hypothesis which is verified by such a procedure. What is verified is a deduction from the hypothesis. The hypothesis itself can never be verified, if by verified is meant shown to be true. It is obvious that however many of the deductions which it is possible to make from a hypothesis may be shown to be consistent with experience, the hypothesis itself retains an element of uncertainty. We can never be sure that sooner or later a deduction from it will not be at variance with the facts and the hypothesis thus shown to be untrue and at least in need of modification. Nor can we ever be sure that a totally different hypothesis will not prove equally successful.

When the question is actually put specifically, most people tend to pay lip service to the view that all scientific theories are, in some degree, uncertain. In practice, however, it is to be feared that they push the question into the background and accept the theories as, for all practical purposes, fully confirmed. Whatever doubt may remain attached to them seems so small that it is safe to assume that it is negligible. The evidence is overwhelming. This appears to be particularly true of those theories which we meet at an elementary level or through popular or semi-popular accounts, in fields in which we are not directly engaged in research ourselves. It may well be the case with certain scientific theories that the evidence is overwhelming, but it is certainly not the case with all. Scientific theories differ greatly among themselves. Some are well founded and difficult, in practice, to doubt though we may be prepared to allow that some element of doubt must remain even here. Our picture of the solar system is a case in point. It is extremely difficult to imagine that it can be seriously in error. On the other hand, some theories contain a large element which is purely hypothetical and a few which pass for scientific may be almost entirely so. The theory of the continuous creation of matter comes to mind as an example of those containing a

14

large hypothetical element. Just as there is a literary and artistic judgment which distinguishes works in these fields according to their quality, so surely there should be a judgment in the scientific field capable of grading scientific theories according to their merit. In the case of artistic and literary criticism, judgment is, of necessity, largely subjective. Science, on the other hand, is objective. The ideal at which work in this direction has aimed has always been to develop an objective scientific judgment, about which general agreement would be capable of being reached. It is the object of this and succeeding chapters to discuss the basis on which the building of such a judgment has been attempted.

The group of problems which this question raises centres on one which has occupied the minds of philosophers for some 200 years. It is sometimes known as the problem of Hume, after David Hume (1711–1776) who first raised it; sometimes it is called the problem of induction. The problem of induction may be put in various ways. One of these is to raise the question of generalisation. How may a perfectly general statement, such as that the volume of a given mass of gas is always inversely proportional to its pressure if the temperature remains constant, be justified when only a comparatively few samples have been, in fact, examined? From the nature of the case it is never possible to examine a generalisation exhaustively. If it were, there would be no generalisation. If the statement applied to a limited number of cases, all of which were accessible to test, no problem would arise. This, however, rarely happens in the field of science. We assert a law, such as that of Charles, on the basis of a large but still limited number of observations. The volume of a gas assumes a continuous series of values as the temperature changes. Only a sample of them can be measured. On the basis of that sample the general law is asserted. The argument is not logically valid. Because samples taken from a certain group of things possess a certain property, it does not necessarily follow that all members of the group must possess that property. Nor does it follow that because an object obeys a certain rule on certain occasions it will always do so. Raising the problem in this way may well make it appear academic and of interest to logicians only. The scientist can leave such logic chopping to them. They are unlikely to reach a conclusion and it will keep them happily employed and out of harm's way in perpetuity.

The problem which Hume raised, however, is of more than academic interest to the scientist. Hume distinguished carefully between statements about matters of fact and those concerning abstract concepts such as those of mathematics. The statements of mathematics deal with the logical consequences of the set of axioms with which the subject starts. They are true whatever the nature of the external world. Statements concerning matters of fact depend for their truth on what is, in fact, the case. They can never be shown to be necessarily true on *a priori* grounds. It is necessary to refer to the facts to ascertain whether they are true or not.

What Hume then went on to discuss was the nature of "cause" and "effect". We are in the habit of assigning causes to the phenomena we study and any question concerning causes affects us intimately. Hume's question was how from a given cause we can deduce a given effect. Let him pose it in his own words.

Suppose I see a ball moving in a straight line towards another, I immediately conclude that they will shock and that the second will be in motion. This is the inference from cause to effect, and of this nature are all our reasonings in the conduct of life: on this is founded all our belief in history; and from hence is derived all philosophy excepting only geometry and arithmetic. If we can explain the inference from the shock of two balls, we shall be able to account for this operation of the mind in all instances.

Were a man, such as Adam, created in the full vigour of understanding, without experience, he would never be able to infer motion in the second ball from the motion and impulse of the first. It is not anything that reason sees in the cause which makes us *infer* the effect. Such an inference, were it possible, would amount to a demonstration, as being founded merely on the comparison of ideas. But no inference from cause to effect amounts to a demonstration, of which there is this evident proof. The mind can always *conceive* any effect to follow from any cause, and indeed any event to follow upon another: whatever we *conceive* is possible, at least in a metaphysical sense; but wherever a demonstration takes place, the contrary is impossible, and implies a contradiction. There is no demonstration, therefore, for any conjunction of cause and effect. And this is a principle which is generally allowed by philosophers.

It would have been necessary, therefore, for Adam (if he was not inspired) to have had *experience* of the effect which followed upon the impulse of these two balls. He must have seen, in several instances, that when the one ball struck upon the other, the second always acquired motion. If he had seen a sufficient number of instances of this kind, whenever he saw the one ball moving towards the other, he would always conclude without hesitation that the second would acquire motion. His understanding would anticipate his sight and form a conclusion suitable to his past experience.

It follows, then that all reasonings concerning cause and effect are founded on experience, and that all reasonings from experience are founded upon the supposition that the course of nature will continue uniformly the same. We conclude that like causes, in like circumstances, will always produce like effects. It may now be worth while to consider what determines us to form a conclusion of such infinite consequence.

It is evident that Adam, with all his science, would never be able to *demonstrate* that the course of nature must continue uniformly the same, and that the future must be conformable to the past. What is possible can never be demonstrated to be false: and it is possible the course of nature may change, since we can conceive such a change. Nay I will go further, and assert that he could not so much as prove by any probable arguments that the future must be conformable to the past. All probable arguments are built on the supposition that there is this conformity betwixt the future and the past, and therefore, can never prove it. This conformity is a *matter of fact*, and, if it must be proved, will admit of no proof but from experience. But our experience in the past can be a proof of nothing for the future, but upon a supposition that there is a resemblance betwixt them. This, therefore, is a point which can admit of no proof at all, and which we take for granted without any proof.

We are determined by *custom* alone to suppose the future conformable to the past. ... The powers by which bodies operate are entirely unknown. We perceive only their sensible qualities: and what *reason* have we to think that the same powers will always be conjoined with the same sensible qualities?

It is not, therefore, reason which is the guide of life, but custom. That alone determines the mind, in all instances, to suppose the future conformable to the past. However easy this step may seem, reason would never, to all eternity, be able to make it.*

For a long period after Hume had raised his problem his writings were read solely for the purpose of serving as a target for a series of "refutations". None of these refutations succeeded, however, and Hume's scepticism remains unanswered to this day. All attempts to justify the processes of generalisation from particular instances or the identification of causes of phenomena, have had to be made to include an assumption which is either identical with Hume's condition of the uniformity of nature or capable of filling a similar role. Science cannot begin without some such basic assumption.

Hume's problem having proved intractable we can but note the fact and accept the position that some such assumption as that of the uniformity of nature must be admitted to lie at the basis of the scientific method. Once we admit such an assumption we can turn our attention to other problems with some hope of progress. In doing this we need not castigate ourselves for having abandoned reason. Hume interprets reason as logical demonstration. In this sense it is true that "it is not reason which is the guide of life, but custom". The problem facing the human race, however, is that of deciding upon a course of action. If the future is conformable to the past, then decisions based on reason can be made. If the future is not conformable to the past, no such decisions can be made. It is not known whether or not the future will, in fact, be conformable to the past, but so long as there is even a possible chance that some part of the future may be remotely connected with some part of the past, then

* *An Abstract of a Treatise of Human Nature.*

we are bound to act on the assumption of conformability. Indeed the coefficient of correlation would have to be known to be exactly zero for this line of conduct to be unreasonable. So long as unconformability cannot be demonstrated—and this is obviously as impossible as the demonstration of conformability—this will be the case. It is a question of Hobson's choice. So far as practical action is concerned, therefore, we are driven to disregard the problem, as, in fact, we always do. If science is content with the role of the practical man's guide to the physical world, it can sidestep the problem of Hume. If, however, it has pretensions to supply the "truth", in the sense of providing an unequivocal answer as to the nature of the physical world, then it is bound to come up against the obstacle which Hume first raised, in some form or other.

Hume's problem was raised concerning causes but this is incidental. The statement of a causal uniformity is, in fact, a generalisation to the effect that whenever a certain thing happens then it will be followed by a certain other occurrence. The cause of a man's death may be a bullet through the brain. This is equivalent to the statement that this man has a bullet through his brain combined with the general statement that whenever a man has a bullet through his brain he dies. The two are identical.

There is a third way in which it is possible to pose the problem of the scientific method, which makes it more obviously germane to the development of a scientific judgment. According to the views we have taken so far the scientific method consists in the development of a hypothetico-deductive system. Hypotheses are put forward and tested against experience. However, if in such tests what is verified is not the hypothesis itself but only a deduction from it, what is the effect of such verification on the hypothesis?

It is possible to look at this question from two angles. In practice we are inclined to place more and more reliance upon a hypothesis, the more completely corroborated—in the sense of having deductions made from it checked with experience—it has been. In this way of regarding the question it is taken as a working rule that the hypothesis has had its value increased by the process of testing. This can be of value irrespective of its ultimate truth or falsity. However, testing in this way is often thought to increase the degree of credibility of the hypothesis. This view would seem to imply that our belief in its ultimate truth has been increased. In this case our problem may, therefore, be put as follows. In what way is it legitimate to regard the credibility of the hypothesis as being affected by the verification of its consequences?

As testing proceeds successfully the usefulness and credibility of a hypothesis increase steadily; that at least is the view which we now

wish to examine. In order to do so it is natural to turn to the theory
of probability which is used to compute expectations in the business
world of insurance and in games of chance. In using it we must be
under no illusion that we shall ever be in a position to answer the
problem of Hume by its means. As Hume pointed out, the theory
of probability is built upon the assumption that the future will be
conformable to the past and must include some such proposition as
that affirming the "uniformity of nature" among the axioms from
which it starts. This also is one of the fundamental suppositions of
science, and it is the great achievement of Hume to have recognised
this and pointed it out. As soon as we have resort to the theory of
probability the principle of the uniformity of nature becomes built
into our system and whenever we examine any of the results at which
we arrive it will be inevitable that we shall find it as one of the
conditions of its acceptability.

As we have seen, however, we are left with no alternative but to
act on the assumption that the future will be conformable to the
past and in doing so build into any system we construct the uncertainty inherent in it. Without such an assumption any further
discussion will remain completely sterile on the stony ground of
Humean scepticism. Let us therefore, with humble mind, turn to
the question which then follows. How are our hypotheses affected
as their consequences are successively confirmed?

Chapter IV

THE LAW OF SUCCESSION

The testing of a scientific theory, consisting as it does in the verification of deductions, cannot establish the truth of a theory although
it can falsify one. Nevertheless we have greater confidence in a theory
which has successfully passed a large number of tests than in one
which has been subjected to only a few, and we treat as purely
speculative and unreliable any theory which has not been tested at
all. A problem which has engaged the attention of statisticians is
that of estimating this degree of rational belief and of ascertaining
the effect on it of a series of verifications. Since verification cannot
lead to certainty it can only be probable truth that is increased by
testing, so that it is to the theory of probability that one must turn
if the problem is to be considered

The theory of probability arose from the study of games of chance.
In such games we do not know what the ultimate result will be but
we are prepared to wager our money at certain odds. The odds which
we are prepared to accept indicate our belief in the likelihood of the
desired event turning up. The theory of probability deals with the
question of how this likelihood should be estimated.

The immediate problem which has to be solved at the outset of the
investigation is how such a vague and arbitrary notion as rational
belief is to be measured. The term probability itself is difficult to
define in a way which makes it useful. These difficulties have, indeed,
led many to think that the whole exercise is of little value. It would,
however, be a mistake to abandon the enterprise at this stage. There
are cases, as we shall see, where the theory can be applied without
ambiguity to scientific theories and the result of doing so is to
confirm the validity of the procedures of science in these cases.
Consideration of the theory of probability cannot be omitted from
any review of the possible basis of science.

For the time being we will postpone consideration of the difficulties
which arise over the definition of the term probability and treat it as
a quantity the meaning and method of estimation of which are
familiar. If a die is thrown at hazard any one of its six faces is as
likely to fall uppermost as any other, if the die is made symmetrically.
We estimate the probability of throwing any particular number, say
a three, as one-sixth. We reckon that in a long run one-sixth of the

throws would show a six uppermost, another one sixth a five, and so on for the remaining numbers, four, three, two, and one. In such simple cases the probability of an event is measured by the number of ways in which the event can happen divided by the total number of possible happenings. If there are n possible, (and equally likely) alternatives for m of which p is true, then the probability of p is said to be m/n. This is not strictly a definition of probability because the words in parenthesis "equally likely" mean equally probable. If these words are omitted the probability would be defined exactly but would not correspond to the word as it is normally used. The probability of throwing a six with a die would remain a sixth whether the die was biased or not. In the case of a die we would reckon to be able to tell whether it was biased or not by measuring its faces and noting where the centre of gravity came. If the faces were all equal and the centre of gravity was in the middle we would assume, on the basis of our knowledge of mechanics, that the chance of any one of the faces turning up was the same as that for any other. The question would be judged by symmetry—that is by the absence of significant difference. More complicated cases, however, are much more difficult, if not impossible, to decide in this way.

The first consideration of the application of the theory of probability to the question of the verification of hypotheses was made in a paper by Thomas Bayes. Thomas Bayes died in 1761, and his contribution, entitled *An essay towards solving a problem in the doctrine of chances*, was published after his death. It was communicated to the Royal Society by his friend Richard Price and it appeared in the Philosophical Transactions of the Society in 1763. Price added an introduction of his own in place of the one originally written by Bayes, which has not been preserved.

Bayes' theorem deals with the following problem. Suppose that the probability of an event happening is unknown and that in a subsequent series of n trials it happens in a of them and fails to occur in b, $(n = a + b)$.

What is the probability of its happening in the $(n+1)$th trial? In other words what is the probability of an event *a posteriori*, after the results of a series of trials is known?

Its relevance to the question of scientific inference is that it might give us a method of determining the effect of the results of tests of a theory on the probability that further deductions from it will be true.

Bayes' solution of this problem depends upon a preliminary axiom being granted. It may have been uncertainty about its validity which led Bayes not to publish his work in his lifetime. It has certainly led to later criticisms. The axiom is as follows. In the entire

3

absence of knowledge *a priori* the probability of an event occurring is as likely to have any one of the values between the limits 0 and 1 as any other. The chance of its falling in any range, dp, he assumed to be proportional to dp.

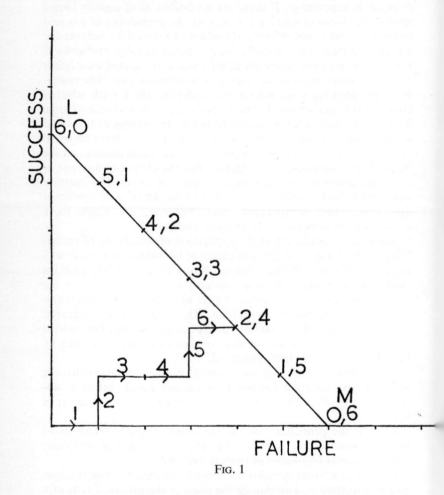

FIG. 1

Let us plot successes and failures in the trials on a diagram, as in Fig. 1, to help our understanding of the argument. We start from the origin, and to record a success we advance one unit vertically upwards. To record a failure we advance horizontally one unit to the right. In any n trials, therefore, we could arrive at any of the $a+b+1$ points on LM whose equation is, $a+b=n$, which possess integral coordinates. In Fig. 1 n has been given the value 6 and a possible route whereby the point $a=2$, $b=4$, may be reached, indicated. This route consists of an initial failure (marked 1) followed by a success (marked 2), followed in turn by two failures (marked 3 and 4), a success (marked 5) and then a failure (marked 6). The event we are considering could happen in two trials and fail in four in a number of ways, since there are several routes which start at the origin and end at the point $a=2$, $b=4$. If we construct a pack of six cards, of which two are marked "success" and four "failure", the number of routes will be equal to the number of ways in which these cards can be dealt out. Irrespective of their markings the cards can be dealt in 6! ways, but since the two cards marked "success" can be interchanged without altering the route it is necessary to divide by 2. The four cards marked "failure" can also be interchanged among themselves without altering the route, and this can be done in 4! ways. The number of different routes which start at the origin and end at the point $a=2$, $b=4$, will be

$$\frac{6!}{2!\,4!}$$

The number of ways of achieving a successes and b failures in a series of $a+b$ trials will thus be

$$\frac{(a+b)!}{a!\,b!}$$

These values are the terms in the binomial expansion $(1+1)^n$. They are a maximum when $a=b$, indicating that other things being equal (i.e., if success and failure are equally likely) we are more likely to arrive at points near the middle of the line LM than at points near the ends.

However, "other things" may not be equal. If our event is the throwing of a six with a die, failure will be more probable than success. Our die may also be biased. If the chance of success in any one trial is p (and that of failure, therefore, $1-p$), the chance of success in the first two trials will be p^2, and of success in the first three p^3, etc. The chance, therefore, of obtaining a successes and b failures, in a given order in a run of n throws, will be

$$p^a.\,(1-p)^b$$

But since a successes and b failures can occur in

$$\frac{(a+b)!}{a!\,b!}$$

different orders the probability of obtaining a successes and b failures irrespective of the order in which they occur, will be

$$\frac{(a+b)!}{a!\,b!}\,p^a\,(1-p)^b$$

The probability of this happening and at the same time the chance of p falling within the range dp is therefore,

$$\frac{(a+b)!}{a!\,b!}\,p^a\,(1-p)^b\,dp \qquad (1)$$

When p is small we shall tend to end up at points near M in our diagram. When p is nearly equal to 1, on the other hand, we shall tend to end up near L. If p ranges over all the values from 0 to 1, then we shall be as likely to end up at any of the points on LM as on any other. There are $a+b+1$ points on LM which possess coordinates which are whole numbers, and thus the probability of ending up at any one of them will be

$$\frac{1}{a+b+1} \qquad (2)$$

In other words, this would be the value of expression (1) when integrated over all values of p from 0 to 1. Thus,

$$\int_0^1 \frac{(a+b)!}{a!\,b!}\,p^a\,(1-p)^b\,dp = \frac{1}{a+b+1} \qquad (3)$$

We can set out the position, therefore, as it appears prior to the trials, by means of the expressions (1) and (2), as in the upper table on p. 25.

The trial then takes place and a successes and b failures are recorded. Let us now construct a second table *a posteriori* showing the probabilities. Since the point (a, b) has been reached, in fact, the probabilities in all the rows except that for a, b, must be zero and that in the third column of the row for a, b, must be unity. It is the value to be entered in the second column of this row that has to be determined. The entry at this point in the original table for prior probabilities will continue to give the relative probability of reaching the point a, b, as the chance of success in single trials is allowed to have all values from 0 to 1. In other words, the probability of reaching a, b, and the initial chance of success in any one event lying between p and $p+dp$, is proportional to

$$\frac{(a+b)!}{a!\,b!}\,p^a(1-p)^b\,dp$$

Prior Probabilities

Point reached	Prior probability of reaching point if chance of success lies between p and $p + \mathrm{d}p$	Prior probability of reaching point if chance of success ranges over all values from 0 to 1
$0, a+b$	$\dfrac{(a+b)!}{(a+b)!}(1-p)^{a+b}\,\mathrm{d}p$	$\dfrac{1}{a+b+1}$
$1, a+b-1$	$\dfrac{(a+b)!}{(a+b-1)!}p(1-p)^{a+b-1}\,\mathrm{d}p$	$\dfrac{1}{a+b+1}$
$2, a+b-2$	$\dfrac{(a+b)!}{2!(a+b-2)!}p^2(1-p)^{a+b-2}\,\mathrm{d}p$	$\dfrac{1}{a+b+1}$
. . . . .	. . . .	. . . . .
a, b	$\dfrac{(a+b)!}{a!\,b!}p^a(1-p)^b\,\mathrm{d}p$	$\dfrac{1}{a+b+1}$
. . . . .	. . . .	. . . . .
$a+b-2,\ \ 2$	$\dfrac{(a+b)!}{(a+b-2)!\,2!}p^{a+b-2}(1-p)^2\,\mathrm{d}p$	$\dfrac{1}{a+b+1}$
$a+b-1,\ \ 1$	$\dfrac{(a+b)!}{(a+b-1)!}p^{a+b-1}(1-p)\,\mathrm{d}p$	$\dfrac{1}{a+b+1}$
$a+b,\ \ \ \ 0$	$\dfrac{(a+b)!}{(a+b)!}p^{a+b}\,\mathrm{d}p$	$\dfrac{1}{a+b+1}$
Total $\quad a+b+1$	$\mathrm{d}p$	1

Posterior Probabilities

Point reached	Posterior probability of reaching point if chance of success lies between p and $p + p$	Posterior probability of reaching point if chance of success ranges over all values from 0 to 1
$0, a+b$	0	0
$1, a+b-1$	0	0
$2, a+b-2$	0	0
. . .	. . .	. . .
a, b	$(a+b+1)\dfrac{(a+b)!}{a!\,b!}p^a(1-p)^b\,\mathrm{d}p$	1
. . .	. . .	. . .
$a+b-2,\ \ 2$	0	0
$a+b-1,\ \ 1$	0	0
$a+b,\ \ \ \ 0$	0	0
Total $\quad a+b+1$	$\dfrac{(a+b+1)!}{a!\,b!}p^a(1-p)^b\,\mathrm{d}p$	1

Since the integral of this for all values of p from 0 to 1 is, as we have seen,

$$\frac{1}{a+b+1}$$

and since the point a, b, having been reached the probability of reaching it (whatever the initial chance of success) must be unity, it follows that the constant of proportionality must be $a+b+1$. The final result is, therefore, that if the prior chance of success, p, were unknown and a trial gave a successes and b failures, then the probability that p had a value lying between p and $p+dp$ is

$$\frac{(a+b+1)!}{a!\,b!}\,p^a(1-p)^b\,dp \tag{4}$$

If the trial were now to be repeated this expression enables us to weight the probabilities of success, in the next trial.

We are now in a position to consider the following question. Suppose that all that is known of an event is that it has happened in a cases and failed in b cases in a series of $a+b$ trials. What is the expectation of success in the succeeding $(a+b+1)$th trial? If we have arrived at the point P in Fig. 2, what is the chance that the next throw will register success and take us to the point Q? If the probability of success is p then this is also the probability of reaching Q in the next trial.

The fact that we have arrived at the point P (a, b) tells us that the probability that the chance of success in a single throw, p, lies between the values p and $p+dp$, is

$$\frac{(a+b+1)!}{a!\,b!}\,p^a(1-p)^b\,dp$$

The probability of reaching Q with a chance of success in an individual throw between p and $p+dp$ will therefore be obtained by multiplying this expression by p. It will, therefore, be

$$\frac{(a+b+1)!}{a!\,b!}\,p^{a+1}(1-p)^b\,dp$$

The probability of reaching Q considering all values of the chance, p, will therefore be

$$\int_0^1 \frac{(a+b+1)!}{a!\,b!}\,p^{a+1}(1-p)^b\,dp = a+1 \int_0^1 \frac{(a+b+1)!}{(a+1)!\,b!}\,p^{a+1}(1-p)^b\,dp$$

the value of which from our previous discussion can easily be seen to be

$$\frac{a+1}{a+b+2}$$

This is the so-called "Law of Succession". It gives the likelihood of an event occurring if all that is known about it is that in a series of n trials it has occurred in a and failed to occur in b. It is often quoted with b assigned the value zero. Thus if all that is known of an event is that so far there have been a occasions on which it could have

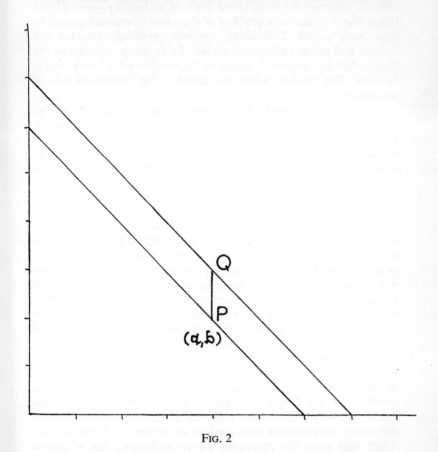

FIG. 2

occurred and that it has happened on all of them, then the chance of it occurring on the next possible occasion will be

$$\frac{a+1}{a+2}$$

It was at one time thought that in the rule of succession a solution to the problem of the scientific method had been found. As successful trial succeeds successful trial and the value of a increases, the chance of success in the next trial following also increases, and indeed rapidly approaches unity. Success could be interpreted as the verification of the consequences of a hypothesis and as these accumulated the likelihood of continued success in the future seemed assured. Granted the basis of the laws of probability—*pace* David Hume that is to say—the problem of the scientific method seemed to have been solved. Difficulties, however, gradually clouded the horizon and initial enthusiasm waned. From being regarded as the long-looked-for answer it came to be considered a snare and a delusion. One modern writer has called it the "notorious rule of succession".*

In criticising the results of the application of a piece of mathematics there are three areas to which attention should be directed. The first comprises the postulates upon which the mathematics is based, the second is the actual process of mathematical deduction itself and the third the application to the example in question. It is an essential part of what might be called the licence of the mathematician that he must be allowed to choose his postulates as he pleases. It is essential to understand what they are but they cannot be questioned except on the grounds of their usefulness—in which the mathematician, as such, has no interest. All that he undertakes to do is to tell us the consequences of accepting them. As far as the next process of mathematical deduction is concerned it is desirable, for our own satisfaction, and in order to be self-reliant, that this should be examined. Mistakes are occasionally made by even the most eminent of mathematicians. The examination of the mathematical deduction, however, is rarely rewarded by the discovery of logical errors, given a reasonable competence in the authors and a thorough check by other mathematicians. It is in the application that the sources of mistakes are most frequently to be found, and particularly in the relation of the application to the initial postulates of the mathematics. It is failure to ensure that the examples chosen fulfil the initial conditions postulated that has given rise to most of the difficulties in connection with the Law of Succession. There is small doubt that given the postulates the result follows, but of course postulates may be such that either no examples which fulfil them can be found in nature, or those that can be found are of little interest. Let us examine some possible cases.

If nothing is known of an event except that it might occur (i.e., there have been no examples of its happening or failure to happen heretofore) $a=0$ and the rule of succession gives the value which ought to be put upon the expectation of its occurring on the first

* G. H. von Wright, *A Treatise on Induction and Probability*, p. 293.

possible occasion to be 1/2. This strikes one immediately as absurd. Suppose a collision between two aeroplanes has never occurred before and for the first time two aeroplanes fly in the neighbourhood of each other. The chance of collision is most certainly nothing like as high as 1/2. The example, however, is not a fair one. It would not be true, even in such a case as that postulated, that the only knowledge we have of aeroplane collisions is that they are possible but so far have not had the opportunity of occurring. We would undoubtedly know a great deal about collisions in general which would affect the probability of one taking place between two given aeroplanes. We would have an idea of their transverse cross-sections, their speed and the times for which they are likely to remain in the air, all of which are factors which would affect the likelihood of a collision occurring while the two machines were flying in the same neighbourhood. It is precisely because we possess such knowledge that the prediction from the rule of succession appears absurd to us.

Venn, a vigorous critic of the rule of succession, gave as examples of its failure the following.*

"I have found it rain on three days successively", implying a criticism of the view that the chance of rain on the fourth is 4/5, as given by the rule of succession. For the rule to be applicable it would be necessary for John Venn to have had no experience of weather whatever except on the three days he mentions, as well as to have found that it rained on each. It is only because he knows, or thinks he knows, more about the weather than he has allowed to be used as the basis for the forecast, that the result appears to him to be absurd. Had he been cast upon a strange shore with an utterly unknown climate from the dark hold of a pirate ship, and had the experience of three consecutive days of rain, the estimate of the chance of a fourth of the same kind does not appear at all unreasonable.

"I have found on three separate occasions that to give my fowls strychnine has caused their deaths", again implying a criticism of the view that the chance of killing fowls on the fourth application would be 4/5. Sir Ronald Fisher has pointed out that the example depends upon the presumption that much more than the 50 per cent lethal dose has been employed. If this is known *a priori* the conditions of the rule of succession are not fulfilled. If it is not, the rule does not give an unreasonable result for the expectation.

"I have given a false alarm of fire on three different occasions and found people come to my help each time." Against the implied criticism of the rule of succession Fisher has pointed out that for the example to work as Venn supposed, it has to be assumed that it is the

* Quoted from R. A. Fisher, *Statistical Methods and Scientific Inference*, p. 25.

same neighbours who are involved on each occasion so that the trials are thus not even independent.

The results of the application of the rule of succession in these and similar cases we may desire to consider, appear absurd solely because we are in possession of more information than we have allowed to be inserted when applying the rule.

The rule has been called in question on grounds of consistency.* As this amounts to a criticism of the mathematics on which it is based, it deserves further consideration. The probability of an event about which nothing is known except that it may or may not happen, is given by the rule to be 1/2, before any trial has been made. If the event occurs in the first trial then the probability that it will occur in the second is 2/3. The chance of the event turning up twice in succession is, therefore, $1/2 \cdot 2/3 = 1/3$, if it has already happened once. But if the trials are independent and the chance of an event happening is 1/2, then the probability of a run of two successive occurrences should be 1/4 and not 1/3. For example the chance of drawing a red card from a pack is 1/2, and that of drawing two red cards in succession is certainly 1/4 and not 1/3. But this is not quite the problem which the rule of succession attempts to solve. Using ordinary playing cards, we know the constitution of the pack from which the draw is to be made. Armed with this knowledge we would certainly not accept odds of two to one against the successive drawing of two red cards. The position contemplated in the rule is that we know nothing, not only about individual cards, so that the draw is a random one, but that we know nothing about the pack from which the draw is to be made as well. We would have to know of the existence of red and black cards in order to know that the drawing of a red card was a possibility, but we would have to be presented with a pack in which we did not know the ratio of red cards to black. The possibility that our pack is not composed of equal numbers of red and black cards has then to be considered. If the pack has been made up at random then the drawing of a red card on the first draw is an indication that there may be a preponderance of red ones in the pack. The chance of a run of two cards of the same colour will clearly exceed 1/4, which is what it would be if the pack were evenly balanced.

Take as an example the throwing of coins drawn from a certain collection. To conform to the rule we have to assume that we do not know whether the coins we are using are double-headed or double-tailed or are normal and possess one head and one tail. Now after a coin has been tossed once and a head has turned up we are in possession of further information which we must use in estimating the chances for the second throw. The information which we have

* Prof. J. O. Wisdom, *Foundations of Inference in Natural Science*, p. 178.

acquired indicates that the particular coin which was tossed cannot belong to the double-tailed class. The probability of throwing a head in the next throw, therefore, cannot extend as low as zero. We are interested in estimating the constitution of the coins from which the throws are to be made. The question we seek to solve is what must be the constitution of the collection so that it is probable that at least one and possibly two heads will be thrown in the first two throws. For this the order of the throws will not be important. The various pairs of throws which are consistent with this information are as follows:

H	T
T	H
H	H

Each of these combinations will be equally likely. Using a collection of coins with this distribution from which to make the next throw we see that the chance of throwing a head will be 2/3, which is in accordance with the rule of succession.

Suppose, as a further example, that three throws have given heads. What will be the chance of obtaining a head with the next throw? Our information is that at least three out of the first four throws will give heads so that the various possible groups of four throws which include at least three heads will be as follows:

H	H	H	T
H	H	T	H
H	T	H	H
T	H	H	H
H	H	H	H

This gives us an estimate for the relative number of heads and tails in the coins we are using. Using coins with such a distribution the probability of throwing a head will be 4/5, as predicted by the rule of succession.

Lastly let us consider similarly the drawing of a red card from a pack. If we know that the pack is evenly distributed and contains equal numbers of red and black cards, the chance of drawing one red card would be estimated to be 1/2 and that of drawing two red cards in succession 1/4, and not 1/3, as Professor Wisdom points out. If, however, we do not know this we must proceed as with the coins. If a red card has been drawn then out of the first two draws one at least will be of a red card. The number of possible pairs consistent with this are,

R	B
R	R
B	R

Each of these will be as likely as any other and such a distribution among the pack is thus to be expected on the information we now possess. The likelihood of drawing a red card from a pack of this composition will be 2/3, as with the coins. The other probabilities given by the law of succession follow in a similar manner.

To confirm this, as a final example let us suppose that one draw has given a red and two draws blacks. What is the chance of drawing a red card in the next throw? The combinations consistent with the drawing of at least one red and two black cards in the first four draws are as follows:

B	B	B	R
B	B	R	B
B	R	B	B
R	B	B	B
B	B	R	R
B	R	B	R
R	B	B	R
B	R	R	B
R	B	R	B
R	R	B	B

This gives 16 reds out of a total of 40 cards. With a pack of such a composition the chance of drawing a red card is 16/40, which is

$$2/5 = \frac{1+1}{1+2+2}$$

and in agreement with the formula of the rule of succession.

The rule of succession has had many unwarranted arguments levelled against it. At the same time many of the questions which it attempts to solve are ones which most people would decline, if at all possible, to attempt to answer. The question examined is what odds should be placed upon an event happening in the case when we know nothing whatever about the nature of the event itself apart from its occurrence on a certain number of occasions and its non-occurrence on a certain number of others. There might conceivably be cases in which it was imperative that action should be taken in such circumstances and when that happened the best we could do would be to act in accordance with the rule. Unless action is imperative, however, such circumstances demand a suspension of judgment. We would decline to offer or accept odds until more was known about the circumstances.

A great deal of the controversy which has revolved round the rule of succession has been about how far games of chance can furnish a useful guide to scientific theories. There is little doubt that the theory applies to games of chance. It could be useful as giving a general indication of the working of the scientific method even though opportunities for its direct application may be small. One opportunity for applying the rule, perhaps, is presented by Bode's law for the radii of the orbits of the planets, to which reference will be made in Chapter VI. No reason has ever been suggested why this rule should hold and, in fact, nothing is known of it except that it works with quite surprising accuracy for planets as far out as Uranus. At the same time we probably have to accept the fact that the rule of succession deals, in the main, with cases which are not quite like those in which scientific interest centres.

It was, at one time, hoped that the rule would furnish a solution to the problem of induction. This it obviously cannot do. The rule is founded upon the laws of probability so that it clearly cannot meet the scepticism of Hume and, since if it is known that the future will cohere with the past the problem of induction presents few difficulties, it cannot solve that problem. At the same time it might, nevertheless, provide an indication as to how, given the basis in induction, scientific argument proceeds. Although it might be capable of being applied to only a few cases of exceptional simplicity, it might still give an indication as to how more complicated cases work, even though it cannot be applied in detail to them. It is often the case that a similar situation arises in connection with scientific theories. They may be capable of accounting in detail for only one or two situations of exceptional simplicity but they may still be suggestive as to the basic mechanism underlying more complicated cases. Such, for example, was the case with Bohr's theory of the hydrogen atom. It failed to cope with more complicated atoms. It has since ceased to be the theory of even the hydrogen atom, but nevertheless, in its time, it pointed out the lines along which solutions to the problems might be sought.

The rule of succession, for example, is capable of throwing some light on the problem of extrapolation. It is clear from common sense considerations that the further we go in space or time, the less certain must our predictions become. The greater the number of intermediate steps which we attempt to pass over without detailed examination, the greater must our uncertainty become.

Suppose that in the $a+b$ trials which have already taken place there have been, as before, a successes and b failures, so that we have arrived at the point a, b in Fig. 3. If now a further N trials take place it is clear that we are liable to arrive at any of the $N+1$ points between C and D on the line $x+y=a+b+N$. The greater

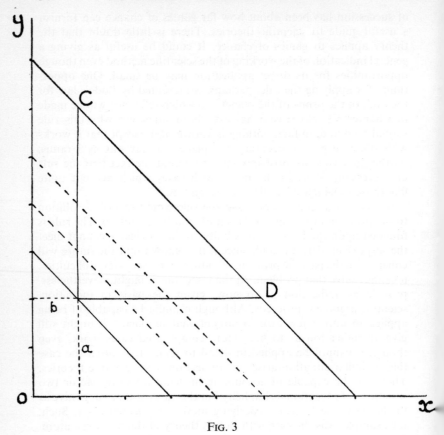

FIG. 3

the value of N the longer will CD become and the greater will be the number of possible points at which the trial could terminate.

The rule of succession gives for the chance of a further success after a successes and b failures have occurred in $a+b$ trials the value,

$$\frac{a+1}{a+b+2}$$

The chance of failure will be

$$1-\frac{a+1}{a+b+2} = \frac{b+1}{a+b+2}$$

The chance, therefore, of achieving N successes in the next N

trials and thus arriving at the point C will be

$$\left(\frac{a+1}{a+b+2}\right)^N$$

The chance of obtaining $N-1$ successes and one failure will be

$$\frac{N!}{(N-1)!\,1!}\frac{(a+1)^{N-1}(b+1)}{(a+b+2)^N}$$

and of obtaining $N-r$ successes and r failures,

$$\frac{N!}{(N-r)!\,r!}\frac{(a+1)^{N-r}(b+1)^r}{(a+b+2)^N}$$

The chance of arriving at the point D will be,

$$\left(\frac{b+1}{a+b+2}\right)^N$$

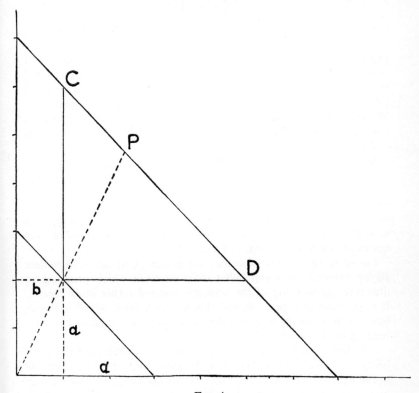

FIG. 4

These are the values of the terms in the binomial expansion of

$$\left(\frac{a+1}{a+b+2}+\frac{b+1}{a+b+2}\right)^N$$

The number of the largest term in this expansion, counting from and including the first at C, will be the nearest integer exceeding the value of

$$\frac{N+1}{\dfrac{a+1}{b+1}+1} = \frac{(N+1)(b+1)}{a+b+2}$$

When a and b are both large compared with unity this term will divide the line CD in the ratio of b to a, as does P in Fig. 4. The most probable result simply continues the same run of successes and failures that we have experienced already. This is what we would expect. There will, of course, be a distribution on each side of P, of points at which there is a finite chance of ending. These will cover the whole range of CD. The chance of reaching any of these points will increase as the point P is approached from either side.

When a and b are small, however, the point possessing the greatest probability does not occur at P but is shifted nearer the mid-point of CD. This again is to be expected since the uncertainty occasioned by the smallness of the number of trials already carried out will introduce a greater possibility of randomness into the prediction. When $a=b$, of course, the distribution will be symmetrical and the point of maximum probability will coincide with P at the mid-point of CD.

If it is accepted that the rule of succession can be applied to scientific theories, then what it would tell us would be the probability of new deductions turning out to be correct. But correct predictions are possible on the basis of incorrect theories and the rule gives no indication about the truth or otherwise of the theory, though it is usually assumed to be the case that verification of its consequences enhances the probable truth of a theory.

Let us leave the rule of succession at this point and reformulate Bayes' theorem in a somewhat different form which promises to illustrate the working of the scientific method rather more clearly. It is possible to express Bayes' theorem in a form which indicates how the probability of a theorem being true is altered as evidence bearing upon it accrues.

All theories must start their existence with some probability of being true, however small this may be, prior to their being examined in the light of evidence which may be forthcoming. The problem of how to assign such an initial probability has so far not been solved.

To pursue the other line of enquiry and examine how the question of probability may throw some light on the method of scientific thinking, it is necessary to leave that question unanswered and turn to certain cases in which initial probabilities are assignable in a manner which is commonly acceptable. The assignation involves the method of induction so that once again no solution to that problem is to be expected. All we can hope for is to illustrate some of the processes involved. In order to do that we must first put Bayes' theorem into a form in which the prior probability is supposed known. It will then furnish information about changes in its value as confirmation of deductions from the theory is obtained.

Appendix to Chapter IV

The examples of the drawing of a card from a pack or the tossing of coins suggests a simple method for deriving the rule of succession. A card is drawn from a pack and it turns out to be red. How does this fact influence the probability of the next card drawn being a red? The answer to this question depends upon how much informaton about the pack we allow ourselves to start with. The problem cannot be answered at all in the complete absence of knowledge except for this event. If we have no knowledge whatever of cards and are unaware of the existence of cards other than red, then the best estimate that we can make is that the second draw will be like the first. If we know that the pack is an ordinary one consisting of equal numbers of reds and blacks, the chance of drawing a red card on the second draw will remain unaffected by the result of the first, assuming that the cards are replaced after each draw. In the rule of succession, we assume that we know of the existence of red and black cards but that we do not know the proportion in which they occur in the given pack.

If our sample draws are numerous enough we would assume that the composition of the pack corresponded to the proportions of reds and blacks occurring in the sample. With a small number of sample draws, this is not good enough. For example, for the second draw it would indicate that the drawing of a red card on the second draw would be a certainty. We therefore proceed as in the examples on pp. 31-32. After a red has been drawn in the first draw the result of the first two draws will be at least one and possibly two reds. Two red cards can be drawn in only one way in the first two draws—each draw must provide a red card. One red card could occur in two ways—on either the first or second draw. The composition of the pack according to such a distribution would be,

$$1 \times 2 + 2 \times 1 \text{ reds and } 2 \times 1 \text{ blacks.}$$

The chance of drawing a red card with a pack of this distribution would be $4/6 = 2/3$, as we have seen already.

If $a+b$ draws have been made, of which a have given reds and b blacks, the result of $a+b+1$ draws, on similar reasoning, would be to give either $a+1$ reds and b blacks, or a reds and $b+1$ blacks.

The number of ways in which $a+1$ reds could be made in the draws is

$$\frac{(a+b+1)!}{(a+1)!\,b!}$$

and they would contain

$$\frac{(a+b+1)!}{(a+1)!\,b!}(a+1)$$

red cards in all.

Similarly the number of way in which a red cards could be drawn would be

$$\frac{(a+b+1)!}{a!\,(b+1)\,!}$$

and they would contain

$$\frac{(a+b+1)!}{a!(b+1)!}a$$

red cards. The total number of red cards would be

$$\frac{(a+b+1)!}{a!\,b!}\left(1+\frac{a}{b+1}\right)$$

$$=\frac{(a+b+1)!}{a!\,b!}\frac{a+b+1}{b+1}$$

Similarly the number of black cards in these draws would be

$$\frac{(a+b+1)!}{a!\,b!}\frac{a+b+1}{a+1}$$

The proportion of red cards is

$$\frac{\dfrac{1}{b+1}}{\dfrac{1}{b+1}+\dfrac{1}{a+1}}=\frac{a+1}{a+b+2}$$

The rule of succession gives this proportion as the probable constitution of the pack for the $(a+b+1)$th draw. This fraction is thus also the probability of drawing a red card on this draw.

Chapter V

BAYES' THEOREM

In modern notation, Bayes' theorem is as follows. Suppose there is an event, p, the probability of the occurrence of which on the basis of existing information, h, may be written

$$p/h$$

and a second event, q, occurs which affects the estimation of the probability of p. Let the posterior probability of p, subsequent to the occurrence of q, be written.

$$p/qh$$

If the probability of the event q, given that p has occurred, is written

$$q/ph$$

and its probability irrespective of the occurrence of p,

$$q/h$$

then Bayes' theorem is,

$$p/qh = \frac{p/h \cdot q/ph}{q/h}$$

If we confine ourselves to games of chance or random events there is little difficulty in seeing the validity of the theorem. Suppose, for example, we have N urns, each containing n_1, n_2, ... balls respectively, of which r_1, r_2, ... are red and the rest white and a draw is made at random. It is found to be a red ball. What is the chance that it came from the sth urn?

The proportion of red and white balls in the various urns will clearly have a bearing on the question, for if it were known that all the balls in one of the urns were white it would be clear that the draw could not have been made from that one. On the other hand, if it were known that all the red balls were concentrated in one particular urn, then it would follow immediately that the draw must have come from that one.

In the general case we could take for p/h the chance of the draw having been made from the sth urn before anything is known about the colour of the ball drawn. The new fact, q, could be the fact that when the draw was made the ball is seen to be red. Thus q/ph would be the probability of drawing a red ball if p is true—i.e., if the draw were known to have come from the sth urn, while q/h would be the probability of drawing a red ball from any urn.

The product of the prior chance of going to the sth urn and the chance of drawing a red ball once the sth urn has been selected,

$$(p/h)\,(q/ph)$$

is the probability of drawing a red ball from the sth urn. That is, of a large number of draws it would be expected that this fraction would consist of red balls from this urn.

q/h would represent the probability of drawing a red ball irrespective of the urn from which it came. Thus this fraction of all the draws would yield red balls.

Thus it is obvious that the probability that the ball drawn, knowing it to be red, came from the sth urn is,

$$p/qh = \frac{(p/h)(q/ph)}{q/h}$$

There is not much difficulty about Bayes' theorem so long as we are dealing with events which can be judged to be random on grounds such as symmetry, such as throwing dice, drawing balls at random from urns, or cards from packs. For example, a card has been lost from an ordinary pack. Two cards are drawn at random from the remainder and found to be spades. What is the chance that the lost card is a spade?

Here the prior probability of the lost card being a spade is

$$p/h = 1/4$$

If a spade has been lost the chance of drawing two spades consecutively from the remainder is

$$p/qh = \frac{12.11}{51.50}$$

We have now to estimate the chance of drawing two spades whether the lost card was a spade or not.

The chance of the lost card being a spade and two spades being drawn is $\frac{1}{4} \cdot \frac{12.11}{51.50}$. The chance of doing the same if the lost card was a heart, diamond or club is $\frac{3}{4} \cdot \frac{13.12}{51.50}$, so that the chance of drawing two spades whatever the suit of the lost card is

$$q/h = \frac{12.11 + 3.13.12}{4.51.50}$$

Thus the chance of the lost card being a spade is,

$$p/qh = \frac{(p/h)(q/ph)}{q/h} = \frac{\dfrac{1}{4} \cdot \dfrac{12.11}{51.50}}{\dfrac{12.11 + 3.13.12}{4.51.50}}$$

$$= \frac{11}{50}$$

A letter is received which is known to have come from Bournemouth, Weymouth or Exmouth. Only the consecutive letters OU can be deciphered in the postmark. What is the chance that the letter came from Bournemouth?

There are 10 consecutive pairs of letters in the word Bournemouth of which two are OU. There are 7 pairs in the word Weymouth of which one is OU, and 6 in the word Exmouth of which again one is OU.

The initial probability of the letter coming from Bournemouth is 1/3. If the letter did, in fact, come from Bournemouth, the chance of the two consecutive letters in the postmark being OU is 2/10. If the letter came from Weymouth or Exmouth, the chances of the consecutive letters being OU are 1/7 and 1/6 respectively. Thus the posterior probability of the letter coming from Bournemouth after the postmark has been seen is

$$\frac{\dfrac{1}{3} \cdot \dfrac{1}{5}}{\dfrac{1}{3} \cdot \dfrac{1}{5} + \dfrac{1}{3} \cdot \dfrac{1}{7} + \dfrac{1}{3} \cdot \dfrac{1}{6}} = \frac{42}{107}$$

The chance of its having come from Weymouth is

$$\frac{\dfrac{1}{3} \cdot \dfrac{1}{7}}{\dfrac{1}{3} \cdot \dfrac{1}{5} + \dfrac{1}{3} \cdot \dfrac{1}{7} + \dfrac{1}{3} \cdot \dfrac{1}{6}} = \frac{30}{107}$$

and from Exmouth,

$$\frac{\dfrac{1}{3} \cdot \dfrac{1}{6}}{\dfrac{1}{3} \cdot \dfrac{1}{5} + \dfrac{1}{3} \cdot \dfrac{1}{7} + \dfrac{1}{3} \cdot \dfrac{1}{6}} = \frac{35}{107}$$

The theory of genetics deals with the random combination of genes and affords examples of scientific theories to which Bayes' theorem can be applied without much doubt or difficulty. In the case of those organisms which reproduce sexually each body cell will contain two sets of chromosomes, derived respectively from each of its parents. On the chromosomes occur the genes which carry factors determining various characteristics of the organism. Thus whether a pea plant will be tall or dwarf, for example, is determined by the combination of a pair of factors, one member being derived from one parent and the other from the other. Thus the gene from one parent may carry the factor for tallness while its partner, derived from the other parent, carries the factor for dwarfness. If both genes carry the same factor the organism is said to homozygous for that factor. If they carry different factors it is said to be heterozygous.

A heterozygous organism may possess characters which are intermediate between those of the two homozygous organisms. However, it frequently happens that the presence of one factor masks the effect of the other. This is the case with tallness and dwarfness in pea plants, the former masking the effect of the latter. The factor for tallness is thus said to be dominant. When dominance is complete, as it is with the tall and dwarf peas, there is no outward difference between the heterozygous organism and the homozygous dominant. The two are indistinguishable.

It is at fertilisation that the two sets of factors are brought together. A homozygous organism produces genes governing a given character, which are all alike. A heterozygous organism produces genes of two kinds. Organisms thus breed true for all characters for which they are homozygous. Heterozygous organisms, on the other hand, do not breed true. The reason is easily made clear by means of the usual notation.

Let X stand for a particular factor—say that for tallness in pea plants—and let x stand for the factor for dwarfness. A homozygous tall plant will be represented by the symbol XX, both its genes carrying the factor for tallness. When a daughter plant arises as the offspring of two such plants, it will derive one factor from one parent and the other from the other, but both will be the same and thus its genetic constitution will be XX, like its parents. The same will be true for homozygous plants carrying the factor for dwarfness, x.

When a homozygous plant carrying the factor X is crossed with a homozygous plant carrying the factor x, the offspring will be heterozygous with a genetic constitution Xx. If X is dominant, as with tallness in peas, all the offspring will appear like the dominant parent.

If heterozygous plants are bred among themselves the characters separate according to the laws of chance. Thus the progeny of plants with a genetic constitution *Xx* will be one-quarter homozygous with the constitution *XX*, one-quarter homozygous with a constitution *xx*, and half heterozygous with a constitution *Xx*. If *X* stands for tallness in peas, then the heterozygous plants will look like their dominant parent and be tall. Thus the result of a cross between peas heterozygous for tallness will be 3/4 tall plants and 1/4 dwarf. Of the tall plants, 1/3 will be homozygous and breed true for this character while the remaining 2/3 will be heterozygous. This can easily be seen with the help of Fig. 5.

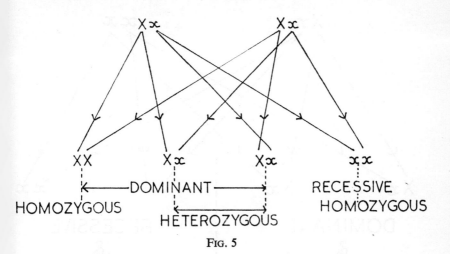

Fig. 5

If a heterozygous plant, *Xx*, is crossed with one which is homozygous for the recessive factor, i.e. *xx*, then half the progeny will be heterozygous, *Xx*, and will be tall, while half will be homozygously recessive and have the constitution *xx* and be dwarf. This can be seen from Fig. 6.

If, in a breeding experiment, a parent showing dominant characteristics has been crossed with a homozygous recessive and individuals with the recessive character appear among the offspring, the dominant parent must have been heterozygous for this factor. The genetic constitution of an organism may be known from its parentage or it may be tested by breeding from it. It is in connection with such experiments that Bayes' theorem finds applications.

For example, suppose that a black mouse derived from the union of two heterozygous parents is back-crossed with another mouse which is homozygous for brown coat colour—the recessive character.

Black is dominant to brown. The result of the mating is, say, five mice showing the dominant black characteristic. What is the chance that the black mouse under test is homozygous?

A priori, as may be seen from Fig. 5 there is a 1/3 chance that a black mouse derived from a cross between two black heterozygous mice will be homozygous, since black is dominant to brown. Thus,

$$p/h = 1/3$$

If it is homozygous all its progeny will possess the dominant character and appear black. Thus

$$q/ph = 1$$

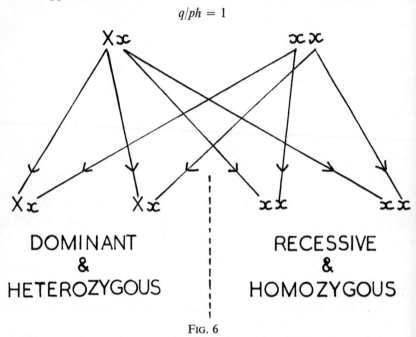

DOMINANT
&
HETEROZYGOUS

RECESSIVE
&
HOMOZYGOUS

Fig. 6

Its prior chance of being heterozygous may similarly be seen from Fig. 5 to be 2/3 and, if it is heterozygous, the chance of any of its offspring showing dominant characteristics when it is crossed with a pure recessive will be 1/2 (see Fig. 6). The chance of five black offspring in such a case will be $1/2^5 = 1/32$.

Thus the probability that the mouse was homozygous is

$$\frac{\frac{1}{3} \cdot 1}{\frac{1}{3} \cdot 1 + \frac{2}{3} \cdot \frac{1}{32}} = \frac{16}{17}$$

The probability that the mouse was heterozygous is

$$\frac{\frac{2}{3}\cdot\frac{1}{32}}{\frac{1}{3}\cdot1+\frac{2}{3}\cdot\frac{1}{32}}=\frac{1}{17}$$

Thus the result of the breeding experiment is to change the probability of the mouse being homozygous from 1/3 to 16/17 and from being heterozygous from 2/3 to 1/17. With a heterozygous parent the chance of a recessive appearing among the offspring of a back-cross with a pure recessive is high. When one does not appear in the litter, the chance of the parent being heterozygous diminishes very rapidly. The chance that the parent was homozygous, of course, increases correspondingly. Thus we see that the degree to which a hypothesis is confirmed by a new observation is greater the greater the certainty with which the observation can be predicted and the smaller the probability of its being true for other reasons. If a hypothesis predicts something which is very unlikely to occur unless the hypothesis is correct, then the confirmation of the prediction very greatly increases the probability of the hypothesis being true.

It is of interest to note that had the original mouse been crossed with a heterozygous black mouse instead of with a homozygous brown one, the results, although furnishing some indication of the genetical constitution of the animal under test, would have been much less conclusive.

If the original mouse was heterozygous, Xx, and it was crossed with another which was also heterozygous, three-quarters of the offspring would be expected to appear with the dominant black characteristic, as indicated in Fig. 5. Thus the chance of obtaining five dominants successively would be $(3/4)^5$ which is equal to 234/1024.

If the original mouse was homozygous, XX, when it was crossed with a heterozygous mouse, Xx, all the offspring would show the dominant character, since they would all carry at least one factor X.

Thus starting with a prior probability of 2/3 of being heterozygous, the probability after producing a litter of five black offspring, would be,

$$\frac{\frac{2}{3}\cdot\left(\frac{3}{4}\right)^5}{\frac{2}{3}\cdot\left(\frac{3}{4}\right)^5+\frac{1}{3}\cdot1}=\frac{243}{755}$$

which is a little less than 1/3.

Similarly starting with a prior probability of 1/3 of being homozygous, the posterior probability would be,

$$\frac{\frac{1}{3} \cdot 1}{\frac{2}{3} \cdot \left(\frac{3}{4}\right)^5 + \frac{1}{3} \cdot 1} = \frac{512}{755}$$

which is slightly greater than 2/3.

Thus instead of yielding a probability of being homozygous equal to 16/17, as when the cross is made with a recessive, the same result from a cross with a heterozygous dominant yields only a probability a little greater than 2/3. The test is much less valuable.

Had the cross been made to a mouse homozygous for the dominant character, all the offspring would have shown the dominant character whatever the genetical constitution of the mouse under test, and no discrimination would have been possible. The posterior probability of the animal being heterozygous would be, in such a case,

$$\frac{\frac{2}{3} \cdot 1}{\frac{2}{3} \cdot 1 + \frac{1}{3} \cdot 1} = \frac{2}{3}$$

which is the same as before the test. Similarly the probability of the mouse under test being homozygous would also remain unchanged at 1/3.

A very interesting and instructive case to which Bayes' theorem is directly applicable is furnished by some experiments of the Abbé Mendel himself, which were subjected to criticism by Sir Ronald Fisher.* It will be remembered that Mendel crossed the dominant tall pea plant with the recessive dwarf variety and obtained plants all of which possessed the dominant characteristic of tallness, but which were all heterozygous. (He used a number of other pairs of characteristics in other similar experiments also.) He then bred a third generation from these cross-bred peas, allowing them to fertilise themselves. The second generation being heterozygous, Xx, the result of "selfing" them is the same as that of crossing a pair of heterozygous plants. Three-quarters of the offspring in the third generation showed the dominant character, as one would expect from the pattern shown in Fig. 5. According to the theory, the dominants should be of two kinds. One-third of them should be homozygous, XX, and two-thirds heterozygous, Xx. In order to

---

* "Has Mendel's Work been Rediscovered?" R. A. Fisher, *Annals of Science*, Vol. 1, No. 2, April 15th, 1936.

test this ratio, Mendel raised, by self-fertilisation, a fourth generation of ten plants from each of the dominant plants in the third generation. If each of the ten plants he obtained in the fourth generation was a dominant, Mendel assumed that the parent plant from the third generation was homozygous. If, of course, a recessive plant appeared in the fourth generation, the parent must obviously have been heterozygous.

The chance of obtaining ten dominant plants from a heterozygous parent, however, is not negligible. The chance of any one of the offspring from such a plant showing the dominant character is 3/4. Thus the chance of obtaining ten in succession is $(3/4)^{10}$. The value of this is about 1/18. We would, therefore, expect about five and a half per cent of the heterozygous dominant plants tested to produce a fourth generation of ten dominants, in addition to all the plants which were homozygous for the dominant character. Mendel, in his experiments, would, therefore, over-estimate the proportion of homozygous plants by between five and six per cent. He did not recognise the importance of this source of error, however. The basis of Fisher's criticism is that Mendel's figures agree closely with what he thought the result should be and depart from those to be expected on the more accurate estimate by an amount which is difficult to account for on the basis of chance fluctuations.

Let us apply Bayes' theorem to this experiment. Let us take one of the plants of the third generation, possessing the dominant characters, at random. According to Fig. 5 the chance of our picking one which is homozygous will be 1/3 and of picking one which is heterozygous will be 2/3. Let us breed ten plants from it and suppose that the result of this experiment is that all the ten are dominants. What is the effect of this on the initial probabilities? Let us take first the hypothesis that the original plant (from the third generation) was a homozygous dominant. Its initial probability is 1/3. If true, the chance of breeding ten dominants from it in as many attempts, is, of course, unity. If, on the other hand, the parent had been heterozygous, the chance of breeding ten dominants would be 1/18.

Thus the posterior probability of the parent plant being homozygous is

$$(p/qh) = \frac{\frac{1}{3} \cdot 1}{\frac{1}{3} \cdot 1 + \frac{2}{3} \cdot \frac{1}{18}} = \frac{9}{10}$$

Here, then, we have an example of a theory which starts off with a comparatively low probability of being true—namely 1/3. *If* it is true then it may be deduced that all the offspring should show the dominant character. Experiment confirms this deduction. As a result, the probability that the theory is true is raised from 1/3 to 9/10.

There can be little doubt about the applicability of Bayes' theorem to a case of this kind. The initial probability of the truth of the theory is capable of being estimated without ambiguity. The likelihood of the experimental result can be calculated precisely, both on the basis of the truth of the theory and on the basis of all other possibilities. The effect of the experimental confirmation of the prediction of the theory is a striking rise in the probability of the truth of the theory from 1/3 beforehand, to 9/10 afterwards. There would appear to be no obvious difference in kind between the confirmation by experiment of a deduction from this theory to which Bayes' theorem can be applied numerically and others, where it is not possible to form precise estimates of the probabilities. This case in genetics might, therefore, be thought to serve as a kind of paradigm example demonstrating the effect which the confirmation of deductions has on the probability of the truth of a hypothesis, in general. We will return to this question in the next chapter.

In the meantime it will be instructive to consider the other alternative theory in the example. This is the hypothesis that the parent plant was heterozygous. Indeed, *a priori*, this is the more likely view to adopt, having a prior probability, according to Fig. 5, of 2/3. The experiment of breeding ten plants from it is performed and they all turn out, let us suppose, to show the dominant character as before. On this theory the chance of obtaining all ten offspring showing the dominant character out of the ten plants bred is 1/18. The posterior probability of the hypothesis being true is thus,

$$\frac{\frac{2}{3}\cdot\frac{1}{18}}{\frac{1}{3}\cdot 1 + \frac{2}{3}\cdot\frac{1}{18}} = \frac{1}{10}$$

The experiment leads to a striking fall in the probability that this hypothesis is true. The betting swings sharply away from this theory in favour of its rival.

Now the interesting point here is that the second theory, namely that the parent plant is heterozygous, is, like the first hypothesis, also capable of accounting for the fact that ten successive offspring show the dominant character. The deduction which can be made from the second theory is that 17/18 of such groups of ten offspring would be expected to contain one or more plants with recessive characters, and 1/18 of them would consist entirely of plants showing the dominant character only. The occurrence of groups of ten dominant offspring is thus a deduction from the second theory as well as from the first. Yet the confirmation of this deduction by experiment actually leads to a striking fall in the probability of the truth of the theory from which it is made. The difference between the two theories is that the first predicts the experimental result as one which follows with certainty from the truth of the theory, whereas the second predicts it as a somewhat unlikely occurrence.

The moral of this would appear to be that, in assessing the effect of the confirmation of a deduction on the likelihood that a hypothesis is true, not only must the confirmation of the prediction be examined but so also must the nature of the prediction itself. Mendel's theory, for example, is quite capable of accounting for the results he recorded in the experiments we have been discussing, which agreed closely with the state of affairs as he imagined they should be, and which brought down on his head the criticisms of Fisher, but it would account for them as a rather rare occurrence in a run of such tests. Instead, therefore, of increasing the probability that his theory is true, as Mendel himself imagined, the experimental results may well, in fact, have diminished it.

Fisher suggested that an explanation of Mendel's results could be that an assistant who knew the results expected, "cooked" the numbers to agree. Such action is by no means unknown. Assistants often feel responsible for the "success" of experiments they set up and that they would even lose their jobs if the experiments failed to produce the expected results. In most experimental work, however, there is a predisposition favouring confirmation rather than rejection of a plausible theory, which if not carefully guarded against can vitiate the results. It does not arise from dishonesty of any kind. If our results do not agree with theory we search diligently for the source of the discrepancy. We check our calculations afresh and repeat our measurements to make certain. On the other hand, if agreement is secured, the necessity for further investigation appears much less urgent and the mind turns to other problems. The counting of biological samples also is not always as simple as it sounds. Variation occurs on account of nurture as well as nature, and plants may differ with regard to other characters which can obscure the issue. A tall plant which has done badly might be confused with a dwarf which has done well and all this affords opportunity for a predisposition in favour of confirming our hunches to exert an influence.

Chapter VI

INDUCTION AND THE
THEORY OF PROBABILITY

So far we have seen that Bayes' theorem appears to be applicable to games of chance and to certain experiments in genetics. The rule of succession, a deduction from the theorem, also refers to similar cases, but it is difficult to find actual examples of much interest elsewhere to which it can be applied directly. The example of genetics seemed to indicate that although Bayes' theorem might not be directly applicable to many other scientific theories because of the difficulty in estimating the probabilities involved, yet nevertheless it might be able, at least in a qualitative manner, to show how the scientific method, by repeated confirmations of predictions, can multiply the probability of a theory being true by a series of factors, which could lead ultimately to the value approaching unity. This appears to have been the view of Richard Price, and he expressed it in the preface he wrote to the paper of Bayes, and which he substituted for the original one composed by the author himself. Whether Bayes held the same view is not known. It is fairly obvious that his interest in the problem must have extended beyond the question of simple games of chance, but his hesitation in publishing his paper may indicate a greater degree of caution.

Bertrand Russell gives an example of an attempt to apply Bayes' theorem to a scientific theory in which only some of the probabilities required can be estimated accurately, which illustrates some of the difficulties as well as the possibilities in applying the theorem. The example he chose was the discovery of Neptune through observation of the perturbations of the orbit of Uranus. The story is well known. Uranus—the first planet to be "discovered", the others then known to exist having all been observed in antiquity—was found by William Herschel on 13th March, 1781, in the course of a systematic sweep of the heavens with his $6\frac{1}{2}$ inch reflector. He thought at first that it was a comet, but after a further five months Laplace showed it to be a new planet beyond Saturn. The name Uranus was suggested by Bode. To the naked eye the planet appears as a very faint star of the sixth magnitude.

After its discovery it was later found to have been observed at least twenty times before, but it had been mistaken for a star. The previous observations, which went back to one by Flamsteed in 1690, were not of high accuracy, but since they covered a complete revolution it was thought they might prove of value in computing an orbit. However, it turned out that it was impossible to satisfy both the old and the new observations and so an orbit was computed by Bouvard on the basis of the new readings only. It was soon found, however, that the planet was not in the position indicated by Bouvard's tables. Bessel went into the matter and suggested that the discrepancies could be accounted for on the basis of perturbations of Uranus by another planet lying still further out from the sun. Adams in England and Leverrier in France computed the position of the hypothetical planet. Adams completed his work first and sent his results to the Astronomer Royal at Greenwich, but the Astronomer Royal had never heard of the young man and procrastinated. He had no map of that particular part of the heavens! Leverrier was luckier. He sent his calculations to an assistant observer at the Berlin Observatory, named Galle. The same night the planet was discovered in the position predicted for it by both Adams and Leverrier.

Here we have a remarkably successful confirmation of theory by observation. Neptune was predicted by the theory of gravitation on the basis of the perturbations in the orbit of Uranus. It is impossible to assign an exact probability to the theory of gravitation prior to the discovery of Neptune, but in order to apply Bayes' theorem Russell assumes, for the sake of argument, that it was as low as the chance of throwing double sixes with two dice—namely 1/36. Our new fact, q, is here the discovery of Neptune. Given the theory of gravitation and the perturbations in the orbit of Uranus, the existence of Neptune is a deduction, and thus, on the basis of the truth of the theory, it would have the probability, q/ph, of unity. It is necessary, however, also to estimate the probability of the existence of Neptune on other grounds. Such were not altogether lacking. Bode's Law, for which, as mentioned earlier, no theoretical explanation has ever been found, gives an estimate of the radii of the planetary orbits. It had been found to work, to a somewhat rough though still rather surprising order of accuracy, as far as Uranus. Later, the asteroids were included in one of the predicted orbits and improved the prediction. Bode's Law was, in fact, employed by both Adams and Leverrier to obtain the rough position of the hypothetical planet they were investigating. The Law is as follows. To the numbers 0, 3, 6, 12, 24, 48, etc., is added the number 4. The result divided by 10 expresses the diameter of the orbits of the planets in terms of the earth's distance as unity. The distance given by the law and the radii of the orbits of the then known planets is given in the following table.

Planet	Radius of Orbit from Bode's Law	Observed Radius of Orbit
Mercury	0·4	0·39
Venus	0·7	0·72
Earth	1·0	1·0
Mars	1·6	1·52
(Asteroids	2·8	about 2·6)
Jupiter	5·2	5·2
Saturn	10·0	9·54
Uranus	19·6	19·18

The discovery of Uranus added a seventh to the list of successful applications—the discovery of the asteroids came later. Bertrand Russell assumes that the probability of Bode's Law applying to the orbit of a hypothetical planet outside that of Uranus, is as low as one-tenth. Bode's Law, however, would appear to be a case to which the law of succession might be applied. Nothing was known about it except that it had worked. It had succeeded in seven of the first eight of its applications and thus the probability of success in the ninth would be given by the law of succession to be

$$\frac{7+1}{8+2} = \frac{4}{5}$$

Let us be generous and assume that Bode's Law would be able to predict the presence of a planet in the orbit occupied by Neptune within the accuracy of the instruments in use. The exact diameter of the orbit is not important. What is important is the chance of finding the planet in the field of a telescope. Given the orbit what would be the chance of finding the planet within say 6′ of the position indicated by Adams and Leverrier? Neglecting possible inclinations of the orbit this would clearly be 1/3600. Thus the posterior probability of the theory of gravitation being true after the discovery of Neptune would be,

$$p/qh = \frac{(p/h)(q/ph)}{q/h}$$

$$= \frac{\dfrac{1}{36} \cdot 1}{\dfrac{1}{36} + \dfrac{1}{3600}}$$

$$= \frac{100}{101}$$

Thus as the result of the confirmation of the prediction the odds on the theory jump from 35 to 1 against to 100 to 1 on. Thus when a prediction made by a theory is confirmed it would appear that the probability of the truth of the theory is multiplied by a factor greater than one, so long as the prediction is of the occurrence of an event possessing a high probability according to the theory. It was thus that Bayes' theorem appeared to provide a basis on which the scientific method could be rested.

It is of interest to notice that the theorem would reject any theory from which a prediction is not in accord with experience. The refutation of a prediction is the same as the confirmation of a contrary fact. A fact contrary to the prediction may be taken to be one which the theory predicts to possess a probability of zero.

Thus $$q/ph = 0$$

But the contrary, q, has been confirmed by observation and thus must be accountable for on some theory. The denominator in Bayes' formula, q/h, therefore, must be other than zero. Thus the posterior probability of the theory being true after one of its predictions has been falsified by observation, is zero, as it should be. It should be noted that this is not to say that future predictions from the theory may not turn out correct. False theories often predict true facts.

There remains the possibility, of course, that no rational explanation exists, in which case the denominator as well as the numerator in Bayes' expression could be zero. The posterior probability would then be indeterminate. This brings to light one of the presuppositions upon which science operates. Science is based upon the assumption that an explanation exists and that it is within the bounds of the human mind to conceive it.

Nevertheless, the employment of Bayes' theorem as a guide to the operation of the scientific method is not without its difficulties.

Some of the difficulty in such wider applications centres round the determination of two of the three quantities which occur on the right-hand side of the formula. As a rule there is not much difficulty over q/ph. The new fact is usually a prediction from the theory and thus its probability, on the basis of the theory being true, is equal to unity. In the case of a statistical prediction as we have seen already, when the new event is predicted to have a low probability, its occurrence in a single trial may lower instead of raising the probability of the theory being true.

With some statistical theories, like those in genetics which we have considered, the prior probability could be estimated without difficulty. It was of the order 1/3 to 2/3 in the cases we investigated in

5

the previous chapter. Also, the theory did not provide exact descriptions of the situations pertaining to individual cases; it gave only an estimation of chances. In general, however, and particularly in physics, we are more often interested in theories which make exact predictions, predictions which are certain to follow if the theory is true. To enable such predictions to be made the theory must obviously be initially of a more precise character. Its prior probability of being true will, therefore, be likely to be lower. The more exactly we specify a system chosen at random the less likely are we to find it exemplified in nature. According to Bayes' theorem, for a theory to end up with a finite probability of being true it must start with an initial probability which is not infinitesimally small, before anything is known about the truth of its consequences. All that confirmation of its predictions can do is to multiply this initial probability by a certain factor. If the initial probability is zero, no amount of confirmation of deductions will give a different posterior probability. Once we depart from games of chance and certain statistical situations to which the theory is immediately applicable, many find it difficult to see how initial probabilities are to be assigned.

It is at least partly to get over this difficulty that recourse to various *a priori* principles has been advocated. J. M. Keynes put forward a principle of Limitation of Independent Varieties. If the number of possibilities is not infinite then there is a finite chance of hitting upon the correct one by chance. C. D. Broad invented a Principle of Natural Kinds to this end. The Principle of the Uniformity of Nature of an earlier time served very much the same purpose.

Because of this difficulty, Sir Ronald Fisher advocated the dropping of the attempt to apply Bayes' theorem in the general case. In its place he suggested a method he called the fiducial argument. This consists in the application of tests of significance. A very simple example quoted by Fisher will illustrate the working of the method. It is Michell's calculation to show that the stars are not distributed at random over the celestial sphere, based upon the likelihood of finding a group of stars as close together as the Pleiades by chance. The hypothesis that the stars are distributed at random is assumed and the chance of finding a group of six bright stars within the distance from Maia to its fifth nearest neighbour is estimated. A very simple calculation shows that this chance is 1/33,000. At this level of significance we would confidently reject the hypothesis. The rejection is not final. The hypothesis of random distribution is capable of accounting for the existence of a close group of stars like the Pleiades, but it would do so as such an unlikely coincidence that we find this explanation of the occurrence unacceptable. It will be seen that the results of applying such an argument are very much the same as those to be obtained from Bayes' theorem. Predictions of unlikely events lead to the theory becoming less acceptable when the event is found to occur. The difficulty of having to assign a probability to the theory *a priori* is avoided, but it is replaced by the necessity to settle on an arbitrary level of significance for acceptance.

The method is not difficult to apply to the apparently exact theories of physics. Even these theories are never capable of exact test because of the inevitable incidence of errors of measurement. We consider such theories to be rejected if the probability of finding the experimental result on the basis of the theory, together with the accompanying errors of experiment, is low. When measurement is accurate the possibility of departing very far from the theoretically predicted values without affecting the acceptability of the theory is small.

Another, and rather more formidable difficulty, arises over the estimation of q/h, the probability of the observed event being true on the basis of any theory. Over how many hypotheses is this to be distributed? In the case of the genetical theories which we considered, the possibilities were limited in number and were known, but by what right can we arrive at a similar conclusion in the case of any of the major theories of science? It is true that the number of major alternatives that we can think of is usually extremely limited, but this may merely reflect the limitations of the power of the human mind. The problem of being sure that in making the estimate all possible explanations have been taken into account is fraught with serious difficulty.

Sir Harold Jeffreys has an answer which side steps this objection to some extent. It is as follows. Bayes' theorem gives for the probability of a hypothesis, p, in the light of one of its deductions, q_1, having been verified, the remainder of the field of relevant information being denoted by H:

$$p/q_1 H = \frac{p/H}{q_1/H}$$

q_1/pH being equal to 1 since q_1 is a deduction from p.

If a second deduction, q_2, from the theory is also verified we have similarly:

$$p/q_2 q_1 H = \frac{p/q_1 H}{q_2/q_1 H}$$

$$= \frac{p/H}{(q_1/H)(q_2/q_1 H)}$$

Similarly for n verifications,

$$p/q_n \ldots q_2 q_1 H = \frac{p/H}{(q_1/H)(q_2/q_1 H)(q_3/q_2 q_1 H)(q_n/q_1 q_2 \ldots q_{n-1} H)}$$

The left-hand side is a probability and must lie between the values 0 and 1. The numerator on the right-hand side must, therefore, always be less than the denominator. Assuming that the theory has some prior probability of being true, there is thus a limit below which

$$(q_1/H)(q_2/q_1 H)(q_3/q_1 q_2 H) \ldots (q_n/q_1 q_2 \ldots q_{n-1} H)$$

cannot fall however many brackets, each of which must be equal to or less than 1, there may be. It follows that after a certain number of verifications have taken place

$$(q_n/q_1 q_2 \ldots q_{n-1} H)$$

must approach unity. That is to say, as the number of verifications of deductions from a hypothesis increases, the chance that the next deduction will be verified approaches unity. Moreover, the result is independent of the hypothesis, p, which does not occur in the result, and it therefore holds whether the hypothesis is true or not. We may thus place confidence in the deductions which can be made from a theory, although we may still remain uncertain about the truth of the theory itself.

Probability theories of the scientific method are likely to make most appeal to those anxious to look upon science as an approach to "truth". Jeffreys' defence of scientific prediction, however, provides a double edged weapon in this respect. While it shows why confidence in deductions made from a successful theory may be justified, its effect upon the confidence which may legitimately be placed in the truth of the theory itself is rather catastrophic. A run of confirmed predictions is possible for an incorrect theory. There are, however, limitations to be considered. Jeffreys' defence given above applies to the confirmation of deductions from the theory so that

$$q/pH = 1$$

If one of the new facts, q_r, say, is only predicted with a certain probability, then its confirmation will multiply the existing probability by a factor

$$\frac{q_r/p, q_1 q_2 \ldots q_{r-1}, H}{q_r/q_1 q_2 \ldots q_{r-1}, H}$$

If q_r is predicted by the theory but as something that has a small probability of occurring, then the numerator of this fraction will be small and there is clearly no necessity for the denominator to approach unity. Also, if in the course of the verifications

$$q_1, q_2, \ldots q_{n-1}$$

previously considered, a substantial number were predicted but with small probability, there is no necessity for

$$(q_n/q_1 q_2 \ldots q_{n-1} H)$$

to approach unity, even though q_n is predicted with certainty as a consequence of the theory. It is necessary, in other words, to look at the nature of the predictions, which is only common sense.

The use of tests of significance also avoids this difficulty. The hypothesis of the random distribution of the stars, examined by Michell, was rejected irrespective of the existence of rival hypotheses to account for the phenomena. It is rejected solely because of our reluctance to accept the fact that an unlikely coincidence has taken place. The choice with which we are always presented in such cases is this: either the hypothesis is incorrect or a highly unlikely coincidence has happened. Of these alternatives we instinctively choose the former. The choice can be justified on the ground that by following such a principle consistently we are likely to be mistaken less often than we would be if we persistently chose the latter alternative. On the other hand to reject a theory before another is available to take its place may not be very helpful. We may still have to employ the theory *faute de mieux*.

It remains to say something about the difficulties encountered in attempting to define what is meant by probability. If there are n possibilities, of which the event whose probability we wish to specify occurs on m, the probability of the event may be defined to be m/n. This gives an unambiguous value to the probability. There are six faces which can lie uppermost when a die is thrown. One of these faces only shows a three. The probability of throwing a three would then be $1/6$. Such a definition would, however, not correspond to what is meant in practice by probability, since it would give the same value whether the die was biased or not. The theory of probability would then be reduced to that of permutations and combinations. In Laplace's definition the alternatives are required to be equally likely. Equally likely means equally probable and so the definition becomes circular. Nevertheless it suffices for the erection of the mathematical deductive system of the theory of probability which then deals with these hypothetical equally likely alternatives.

How these equally likely alternatives are to be recognised in practice is a question left undiscussed, but it is upon this that the application of the mathematical theory to cases of practical interest depends.

We have considered cases in which we would feel little hesitation in saying that a series of equally likely events is being considered. We would form this opinion on the basis of the fact that we were unable to distinguish individual cards in a pack on the basis of the designs on their backs, or individual balls in a bag into which we cannot see, by feeling them. In the case of dice we would endeavour to decide whether or not they were symmetrical. With dice, however, our estimate would be likely to be only rough, and if we were interested in very long runs, as well we might if the odds were to be finely estimated in a game of chance, this method would hardly suffice. We would be brought up against the difficulty directly and we would doubtless try to resolve it by carrying out long experimental runs to see if the dice showed any bias.

This in effect would endow probability with meaning in the sense of a limiting frequency. We would take the probability of throwing an ace to approximate to one-sixth, or whatever value it was found to possess, if, as the number of throws increased, the number in which an ace was recorded tended to the value of one-sixth of the total number of throws made—or whatever fraction was found to obtain in practice.

We may, if we wish, either alter the definition of probability to that of a limiting frequency or we can use our test to find out if the Laplacian conditions are fulfilled in fact. If we alter the definition we shall be assuming that a frequency limit exists. The second alternative is the one which is common with scientific theories of a mathematical character. A piece of mathematics is developed on the assumption of certain idealised situations. Practical tests are then carried out to ascertain whether, in fact, these idealised conditions are to be found in experience. The mathematics requires, as it has been put, a dictionary to enable it to be translated into the world of practical experience, or alternatively the dictionary may be looked upon as allowing the world of practical experience to be translated into the formal language of the mathematics. We thus have the Laplacian mathematical edifice at our disposal if we are able to discern the cases to which it is applicable. We applied the Laplacian mathematics to the case of genetics without hesitation. We were able to do this as a result of the classical experiments of the Abbé Mendel. Before his time it was unknown whether or not inherited characteristics obeyed the laws of chance. It was Mendel who, by means of a long series of experiments, demonstrated that, in fact, at each fertilisation factors controlling genetical characters were recombined at random and thus it is to him that the possibility of applying statistical reasoning to genetics is due. His experiments are thus an exact parallel to the testing of a die by making a large number of trial throws.

For the erection of a logic of inference, however, the definition of probability as a limiting frequency is not altogether satisfactory. It was first introduced by Ellis and Cournot, it was developed by Venn and its chief modern exponents have been R. von Mises and Reichenbach. Venn considers the examination of m alternatives, in l of which the event occurs. The probability of the event is then defined to be the limit to which the ratio, l/m, tends as m is increased indefinitely. While this has the merit of approximating to the procedure often adopted in practice, it is not satisfactory for purposes of definition. In the first place there is no guarantee that such a limit exists and that by prolonging the tests sufficiently the value of the probability will not alter. There is also a chance that a finite sample, however large it may be made, will possess an abnormal constitution. It is *possible* that in throws with a coin all those made in the sample might turn out to be heads. There is an implicit assumption that the larger the sample the nearer the result will be to the series limit. This cannot very well be brought into the open and included among the logical postulates of the system since it is essentially an empirical assertion about what will be found to happen in practice. Logical postulates should not restrict empirical possibilities. Some have attempted to remove the difficulty by referring to infinite populations —Fisher considers a "hypothetical infinite population". In this case there is the difficulty that the ratio of two infinities is indeterminate and it is not clear how this is to be surmounted.

A definition in terms of a limiting frequency would severely restrict the use of the term probability to cases in which an infinite series is available. This would never be the case with scientific theories, which always belong to very limited series because of the limitations of the human mind in thinking of them, and they are not uncommonly unique.

Bayes employed the idea of expectation. This is the product of the gain to be obtained as the result of an event and the likelihood of its occurring. Bayes, in fact, equates the value of a millionth chance of winning a million pounds with the certainty of gaining one pound. In other words he says that the proper price to pay for a millionth chance of becoming a millionaire would be £1. In practice few would agree with him—it would depend upon their present possessions and the value they consequently placed upon the possession of £1. Most would not hazard so much on a practically negligible chance of great riches. In any case it does not help with the definition of probability since expectation includes likelihood.

Carnap distinguishes two probabilities, an epistemological and an intrinsic one. The latter is determined by frequencies; the former measures the degree of rational belief. Again there is some correspondence with common practice. Degree of belief is often based upon frequencies, as insurance companies and their customers exemplify. Most modern writers (as for example von Wright and Kendall) reject a definition of probability as a degree of rational belief. They would maintain that rational belief is incapable of exact estimation and useless for the purpose. They would thus deny the possibility of assigning a probability to a hypothesis which certainly cannot be done on the basis of a definition in terms of frequency.

An exception is Jeffreys, who bases his whole theory on inverse probability, as in Bayes' theorem. He frankly takes induction as fundamental. It is, as he points out, the basis of all learning by experience and should come before deduction, not after it. His aim is to systematise scientific inference by constructing a logical scheme to which it corresponds. His system centres on the acceptance of a degree of rational belief as a primitive notion which is not defined He claims his object is not to justify induction but to "tidy it up". "What we are doing", he says, "is to seek for a set of axioms that will permit the construction of a theory of induction, the axioms themselves being primitive postulates". As we have seen, one way of looking at the theory of probability is to divide it into two parts— the calculus of probabilities and the theory of inference. The calculus of probabilities belongs to pure mathematics and its operations consist in deriving more complicated probabilities from given simpler probabilities by means of the rules for obtaining their sum and their product. Prior probabilities are a formal statement of the information, or lack of it, available at the outset. If there are a number of competing hypotheses about which there is no relevant information initially, the probability is equally distributed among them. Were this not to be done it would amount to prejudice in favour of some of the hypotheses and against the others. The equal distribution of prior probability is thus simply a precise way to recognise and avoid prejudice. The likelihood of an observation on the basis of each hypothesis is estimated and, the observation having been made, the posterior probability is greatest for that hypothesis giving the greatest likelihood.

The Bayes-Jeffreys system thus takes the bold step of incorporating prior knowledge, or the absence of it, at the outset. If probability is regarded as a measure of belief, or an undefined idea obeying the usual postulates, this is unexceptionable. It is, however, hard to reconcile with frequency definitions of probabilities.

Some further discussion of the question of what can be meant by the probability of a unique event—say that of a particular horse winning next Wednesday's Derby, for example—may be worth while. Next Wednesday's Derby has never occurred before and our horse may never have run over the Derby course before, and certainly not in next Wednesday's event. Such a statement of probability, even on the basis of rational belief, can clearly not be confined to this particular event in isolation. The estimate made by the punter of the chances of the horse are based upon its "form", that is upon its performances in other races of similar length and the comparison of the Derby course (whether the going will be soft or otherwise) with courses on which the horse has already run. The definite odds offered by the bookmakers, on the other hand, are not arrived at in this way. They are an attempt to measure public belief. The bookmaker is not a punter; he studies his customers rather than the horses. The odds are low when many hold the view that the horse will win and place their bets accordingly, and high when many think that it hasn't a chance. J. J. Thomson used to tell a story of how, in his undergraduate days, being a mathematician he was sometimes called in by one of the sporting fraternity of his college, to help him in the making of a book. He said that he often found that bets had been accepted in such a way that the bookmaker could not possibly win whatever happened!

Can we assimilate a statement about the probability of a scientific hypothesis being correct to this sort of situation? It is by no means clear how it is to be done. We may not be considering the hypothesis as one of a class of hypotheses and the procedure of the punter with his frequency estimation will not do. Consensus of opinion, even among experts, on the other hand, is an unsatisfactory basis for science, although it has its supporters, so that the method of the bookmakers seems equally inappropriate. The essence of science is that it should be objective and free from dogma. We may wish to treat the hypothesis on its own, no rival having taken the field. This would make us look at a test of significance. We estimate the likelihood of the event which has turned up on the basis of the theory and reject the latter at a given level of significance. The question of why a hypothesis should have to be rejected at a 5 per cent or 1 per cent level of significance, however, remains undecided.

To quote one of the leading authorities, Professor Maurice Kendall: "There is still so much disagreement on this subject that one cannot put forward any set of viewpoints as orthodox. One thing, however, is clear—anyone who rejects Bayes' postulate must put something in its place. The problem which Bayes attempted to solve is supremely important in scientific inference and it scarcely seems possible to have any scientific thought at all without some action, however intuitive and however empirical, to the problem. We are constantly compelled to assess the degree of credence to be accorded to hypotheses on given data; the struggle for existence, in Thiele's phrase, compels us to consult the oracles ".

To return to the theorem of Bayes for a moment, when the probability of an observed event, q/ph, is high on the theory, p, the probability of the theory being true increases. The extent of the increase, however, depends also upon the factor which occurs in the denominator, q/h. Thus a theory benefits by having one of its predictions confirmed when the prediction is difficult to account for in other ways. If the event is easy to account for by means of other hypotheses, then the benefit is less or it may vanish altogether. There seems little doubt that this element does enter psychologically into the degree of confidence which we are prepared to assign to a theory. We saw how this operated in the case of the two rival theories in the genetical example. The theory that the unknown plant with dominant characteristics was heterozygous became difficult to maintain (though not impossible) after all ten of its progeny showed the dominant character, partly because this event, though predicted by the theory, was forecast as an improbable occurrence, but partly because it was comparatively easy to account for the same event on the basis of the alternative hypothesis that the plant was homozygous. Difficulty in accounting for the facts in any other way than by the hypothesis being considered, is undoubtedly an important element in deciding whether to give our allegiance to it or not. Thus where Bayes' theory can be applied it seems likely that it will furnish more information than would a mere test of significance. When an alternative hypothesis is virtually impossible, as is often the case, then the test of significance will contain all the information which the theory of chance can relate to the case in question.

It may be asked why a theory should benefit from the mere difficulty of accounting for a fact on any different basis. Surely this difficulty is one associated with the human mind rather than with the external world. Ought the probability of a scientific theory to be increased because of what may simply be a limitation of the human mind? The fact that we find it difficult to conceive of any other explanation can have very little bearing on the structure of the universe. There is surely no reason to suppose that the world is constructed in such a way that we must be able to understand its mechanism. Indeed, so far as science has progressed at present, the world appears to be a particularly difficult thing to understand and it has been only during the last two hundred years or so that much significant progress towards understanding it has been made. There must be many alternative explanations which, so far, no one has yet put forward. This is a difficulty which is bound to beset those who wish to look upon scientific explanations as describing an independently existing reality. Should there be a very large number of alternative explanations each possessing an infinitesimally small probability of being true, then no amount of confirmation of the deductions from a particular theory will raise its probability of being true significantly.

Ever since the time of Bayes the theory of inverse probability has been the basis for many attempts to explain induction. Such attempts are confronted, as we have seen, by difficulties in the definition of probability, in the assessment of prior probabilities, and in the inclusion of all the relevant theories in the estimation. To surmount these difficulties fresh assumptions appear to be necessary so that the explanation tends to reduce to the replacement of one assumption by another. The most appropriate line to adopt in these circumstances seems to be that of Jeffreys, who accepts the situation and limits himself to systematising it. There seems to be little doubt that apart from a few simple cases direct application of the theory to scientific hypotheses is difficult and that it must rest content with being a description in general terms of the scientific method. There is also a further difficulty to which we shall come later, and that is that scientific hypotheses are not simple and cannot be considered on their own, one at a time. What is verified is the consequence of a number of hypotheses taken together. Such a group of hypotheses is much more plastic than is any one taken in isolation. The group can be modified in various ways so that a different approach to the aims and methods of science may be preferable.

Chapter VII

PROBABILITY IN PRACTICE

Whatever the difficulties which are associated with the logical status of the theory of probability, there is little divergence of view about its application. Statisticians are in agreement about what should be done, though they may appear to differ as to the reasons they have for doing it.

It may help to clarify the assumptions incorporated in the theory if we consider a practical example. A small block of wood was marked so as to make the asymmetrical die of which Plate 1 is a photograph. The faces varied in size, the position of the centre of gravity was not known with any accuracy and it would be quite impossible to calculate the chance that a given face would be thrown. We are therefore forced to have resort to experiment to estimate the chances.

Table 1 on p. 65 shows the results of ten series of throws each of ten individual throws. In the first row, opposite the number of each face is given the number of times it turned up in the particular series of ten throws. In the second row is given the cumulative total throughout the experiment, and in the third row, the cumulative frequency of occurrence—the number of appearances divided by the number of throws.

The numbers 1 and 6 occur on the two largest faces and have clearly the greatest probability of turning up. They turned up three and five times respectively in the first ten throws and thirty and forty-six times respectively in the first hundred. It would appear from this series that the probability of obtaining a one was about 0·30, and of getting a six about 0·46. The number five turned up very infrequently—only once, in fact, in the first hundred throws. This is clearly insufficient evidence on which to base an estimate of the frequency of its occurrence. The number two turned up ten times, which is more than any of the remaining numbers except for one and six. It is still low for an estimate of the frequency.

It is of interest to see how reliable the estimate of 0·30 for the frequency of occurrence of number one and of 0·46 for that of number six turn out to be in further trials. Table 2 shows the results of the next thousand throws, in groups of 100. Little significant change seems to take place in the frequencies of occurrence of the numbers

PLATE I *The unbalanced die*

TABLE 1

Throw	1–10	11–20	21–30	31–40	41–50	51–60	61–70	71–80	81–90	91–100
Number 1	3	2	1	4	4	4	3	1	5	3
Cumulative total.	3	5	6	10	14	18	21	22	27	30
Frequency	0·3	0·25	0·2	0·25	0·28	0·30	0·30	0·275	0·30	0·30
Number 2	0	0	1	2	1	2	1	2	0	1
Cumulative total.	0	0	1	3	4	6	7	9	9	10
Frequency	0	0	0·03	0·075	0·08	0·10	0·10	0·11	0·10	0·10
Number 3	2	0	1	1	0	0	3	0	0	0
Cumulative total.	2	2	3	4	4	4	7	7	7	7
Frequency	0·2	0·1	0·1	0·1	0·08	0·07	0·10	0·09	0·08	0·07
Number 4	0	1	0	1	1	1	0	1	0	1
Cumulative total.	0	1	1	2	3	4	4	5	5	6
Frequency	0	0·05	0·03	0·05	0·06	0·07	0·06	0·06	0·06	0·06
Number 5	0	0	0	0	0	0	0	0	0	1
Cumulative total.	0	0	0	0	0	0	0	0	0	1
Frequency	0	0	0	0	0	0	0	0	0	0·01
Number 6	5	7	7	2	4	3	3	6	5	4
Cumulative total.	5	12	19	21	25	28	31	37	42	46
Frequency	0·5	0·6	0·63	0·525	0·50	0·47	0·43	0·46	0·47	0·46

two, three and four. The number five seems to settle down to a frequency of about 0·04. The frequency of number one, however, shows a tendency to increase, while that of number six tends to diminish, as the test proceeds. To a considerable extent the changes are due to the first hundred throws giving 30 ones and 46 sixes, which were rather exceptional. If the first hundred throws are omitted the frequency for the number one would start at 0·35 and finish at 0·392 while that for the number six would start at 0·37 and finish at 0·348. It is of interest to compare the frequencies estimated in the last column of Table 2 with those of another set of 1,000 throws, which are given in Table 3.

The order of frequency is the same as before but there are small changes in the individual values. The estimate for the chance of throwing a one has dropped from 0·383 to 0·356. The chance of the throwing of a six has dropped from 0·359 to 0·353 while the other numbers occurred rather more frequently than before.

Putting both sets of 1,000 throws together we obtain the values in Table 4.

TABLE 2

Throw	1–100	101–200	201–300	301–400	401–500	501–600	601–700	701–800	801–900	900–1,000
Number 1	30	35	43	35	34	44	36	37	49	40
Cumulative total.	30	65	108	143	177	221	257	294	343	383
Frequency	0·30	0·325	0·360	0·355	0·354	0·369	0·368	0·368	0·381	0·383
Number 2	10	10	8	9	12	7	10	6	9	5
Cumulative total.	10	20	28	37	49	56	66	72	81	86
Frequency	0·10	0·10	0·093	0·093	0·098	0·083	0·093	0·090	0·090	0·086
Number 3	7	4	8	1	5	6	5	6	6	3
Cumulative total.	7	11	19	20	25	31	36	42	48	51
Frequency	0·07	0·055	0·063	0·050	0·050	0·052	0·051	0·053	0·053	0·051
Number 4	6	12	4	6	10	10	6	7	9	9
Cumulative total.	6	18	22	28	38	48	54	61	70	79
Frequency	0·06	0·09	0·073	0·070	0·076	0·080	0·077	0·078	0·078	0·079
Number 5	1	2	3	6	6	5	5	6	2	6
Cumulative total.	1	3	6	12	18	23	28	34	36	42
Frequency	0·01	0·015	0·020	0·030	0·036	0·038	0·040	0·045	0·040	0·042
Number 6	46	37	34	43	33	28	38	38	25	37
Cumulative total.	46	83	117	160	193	221	259	297	322	359
Frequency	0·46	0·415	0·390	0·400	0·386	0·369	0·370	0·371	0·358	0·359

However large the sample may be which we take, there is clearly some chance of getting a frequency of any value from 0 to 1 for any given event. Our sample may be very exceptional. How large a sample ought we to take before the chance of freakish values is small enough to disregard?

Let us look at the first ten throws we made with the die, which gave a total of 5 sixes. Can we estimate what the likelihood would be that this number of sixes would turn up by chance in the first ten throws? Taking probability to be defined by a limiting frequency our total of 2,000 throws would appear to indicate that the chance of throwing a six in any one throw was 0·356. Adopting this estimate, what is the chance of throwing five sixes in ten throws? If p is the probability of an event, we have seen that the chance of its occurring r times in n trials is

$$\frac{n!}{r!\,(n-r)!} \cdot p^r(1-p)^{n-r}$$

TABLE 3

Throw	1–100	101–200	201–300	301–400	401–500	501–600	601–700	701–800	801–900	901–1,000
Number 1	31	34	44	32	39	34	37	30	32	43
Cumulative total.	31	65	109	141	180	214	251	281	313	356
Frequency	0·31	0·325	0·363	0·352	0·360	0·357	0·359	0·351	0·348	0·356
Number 2	7	7	8	6	6	15	10	18	8	8
Cumulative total.	7	14	22	28	34	49	59	77	85	93
Frequency	0·07	0·07	0·073	0·070	0·068	0·082	0·084	0·096	0·094	0·093
Number 3	4	6	4	15	7	4	5	3	6	3
Cumulative total	4	10	14	29	36	40	45	48	54	57
Frequency	0·04	0·05	0·047	0·072	0·072	0·067	0·064	0·060	0·060	0·057
Number 4	9	6	7	9	8	6	7	11	15	7
Cumulative total.	9	15	22	31	39	45	52	63	78	85
Frequency	0·09	0·075	0·073	0·078	0·078	0·075	0·074	0·079	0·087	0·085
Number 5	7	6	2	6	5	3	2	7	5	4
Cumulative total.	7	13	15	21	26	29	31	38	43	47
Frequency	0·07	0·065	0·050	0·053	0·052	0·048	0·043	0·048	0·048	0·047
Number 6	32	41	35	33	35	38	39	31	34	35
Cumulative total.	32	73	108	141	176	214	253	284	318	353
Frequency	0·32	0·365	0·360	0·353	0·352	0·357	0·361	0·355	0·353	0·353

TABLE 4

Throw	1–1,000	1,001–2,000	Total 1–2,000	*Frequency*
Number 1	385	366	749	0·375
Number 2	86	93	179	0·089
Number 3	51	58	109	0·055
Number 4	79	83	162	0·081
Number 5	42	47	89	0·045
Number 6	359	353	712	0·356

Thus the chance of throwing 10 sixes is

$$0.356^{10} = 0.00003$$

The chance of throwing 9 sixes and 1 blank is

$$10.0.356^9.0.644 = 0.00059$$

The chance of throwing 8 sixes and 2 blanks is

$$\frac{10.9}{1.2}.0.356^8.0.644^2 = 0.00482$$

The chance of throwing 7 sixes and 3 blanks is

$$\frac{10.9.8}{1.2.3}.0.356^7.0.644^3 = 0.02323$$

The chance of throwing 6 sixes and 4 blanks is

$$\frac{10.9.8.7}{1.2.3.4}.0.356^6.0.644^4 = 0.07352$$

The chance of throwing 5 sixes and 5 blanks is

$$\frac{10.9.8.7.6}{1.2.3.4.5}.0.365^5.0.644^5 = 0.15961$$

The chance of throwing 4 sixes and 6 blanks is

$$\frac{10.9.8.7}{1.2.3.4}.0.356^4.0.644^6 = 0.24063$$

The chance of throwing 3 sixes and 7 blanks is

$$\frac{10.9.8}{1.2.3}.0.356^3.0.644^7 = 0.24873$$

The chance of throwing 2 sixes and 8 blanks is

$$\frac{10.9}{1.2}.0.356^2.0.644^8 = 0.16874$$

The chance of throwing 1 six and 9 blanks is

$$10.0.356.0.644^9 = 0.06783$$

The chance of throwing no six and 10 blanks is

$$0.644^{10} = 0.01227$$

Thus we see that the chance of throwing exactly five sixes in ten throws is about 0·16, which is about one in six, which is not very unlikely. The chance of throwing five or more sixes in ten throws will be the sum of the first six numbers in the above column of figures. It amounts to about 0·262, which is rather more than one in four. Table 1 shows that in the first hundred throws five or more sixes were thrown five times in the ten groups of ten, twice the number we would expect on the basis of the long run of 2,000 throws on the basis of which we estimated the probability of throwing a six to be 0·356. How likely is it that we may obtain twice the number of five or more sixes that we expect?

To find this out we take as our event the throwing of five or more sixes in ten throws, which we have seen possesses a probability of 0·262, estimated on the basis of our 2,000 throws. The chance of getting this exactly five times in the first ten occasions is

$$\frac{10.9.8.7.6}{1.2.3.4.5}.0 \cdot 262^5 . 0 \cdot 738^5 = 0 \cdot 068$$

Adding up the chances of getting six, seven, eight, nine and ten of these events in the first ten occasions we find that the chance of getting five or more of them is 0·093, or rather less than one in ten. This is a rather small chance though by no means unusual. It raises a question which is typical of those which occur in scientific statistical investigations. Do we accept that this run of a large number of sixes, which was maintained throughout the first hundred throws, occurred by chance or was there something which affected these early throws which could have brought about this result? In other words has the frequency changed during the course of the experiment?

A thing which could bring this about would be wear and tear of the die. This is unlikely to occur in as few as 2,000 throws. On the other hand the die was thrown by hand and it is quite possible that after a certain number, such as a hundred, had been made, tiredness might lead to a different method of throwing having been adopted. An asymmetric die, such as the one which was employed, is sensitive to the method used in the throwing. If it is spun about the axis at right angles to the two large faces carrying the numbers one and six, while this axis is held horizontally during the process, the die is much more likely to come to rest on one of the smaller faces than it is if it is spun about an axis at right angles to this direction, also held horizontally. In the latter case ones and sixes predominate even more markedly, since the die comes to rest on the larger faces more readily. In the actual throws in the above experiment, it was attempted to spin the die about an axis passing through opposite corners to obviate this effect. The spinning may well have changed in character in the course of 2,000 throws.

6

Such questions are never capable of being resolved in a clear-cut manner. We are always faced with the alternative that either an unlikely event has occurred or a factor unaccounted for has been operating. It is quite possible that our run of an unusually large number of sixes occurred purely as a matter of chance. On the other hand it might have been due to the manner of throwing. The question remains an open one. We have, however, a natural reluctance to accept the fact that a *highly* improbable event has occurred. When the odds seem to be weighted against what has happened, according to the view which we take of the mechanism operating, we start to look very carefully at the conditions to see if we have overlooked any factor which might have affected the result.

We will close this chapter, and our consideration of the laws of chance, by discussing the question of departure from the mean or most probable distribution, in a rather more general way. In particular we will examine how the chance of departing from this value depends upon the number of trials made. As we shall utilise the idea of a limiting frequency it will naturally not be possible to prove that, as the number of trials increases, such a limit is, in fact, reached. It has just been seen how difficult it would be to test such a hypothesis. One could never be certain that conditions remained constant. Indeed the only test we have that this is so would be the constancy of the frequency of occurrence, so that it would be extremely difficult to avoid circularity in argument. On the assumption that probability can be measured by means of a finite frequency and that we are dealing with a phenomenon which remains constant throughout, however, we shall be able to see how variation in the sizes of our samples affects the question of the departure from the mean which we are likely to obtain.

Let us consider n throws of a die, the probability of throwing a six on which is equal to p. Let us construct a table similar to those we have just been using. Let us call the individual throws $x, y, z, \cdots$. Let us suppose that the result of the first n throws to be $x_1, y_1, z_1, \cdots$. Then suppose that a second set of n throws is made with the results, $x_2, y_2, z_2, \cdots$. Let this process be repeated a very large number of times. We shall arrive thus at a table of n columns and a very large number of rows as indicated in Table 5.

Each entry in our table will record the number of times that a six turns up. Since the entries refer to individual throws they must be either 1 or 0. Each row will consist of a limited number of throws— say n. We shall, however, have a very large number of rows so that there will be a large number of x's, a large number of y's and similarly of z's, so that when we add up the columns we can use the limiting frequencies.

TABLE 5

Throw	x	y	z	...	...	...
1st Series	x_1	y_1	z_1	...	...	...
2nd Series	x_2	y_2	z_2	...	...	...
3rd Series	x_3	y_3	z_3	...	...	...
4th Series	x_4	y_4	z_4	...	...	...
. . . .	...	...	...	...	...	...
rth Series	x_r	y_r	z_r	...	...	...

If we add up the rows the probable total for the row will be $p.n$, where p is the limiting frequency, but many rows will, of course, show a different total, since we are taking n to be a number of limited size. Each entry will differ from the means by x_1-p, y_1-p, z_1-p, etc., in the first row and similarly for the other rows. These values will sometimes be positive and sometimes negative. On the whole, of course, there will be as many positive as negative but this will not be true for any one row, since the number of throws per row is limited.

The total for the row will be

$$x+y+z+\cdots$$

Thus, if the frequency of the occurrence is estimated from the row, the value obtained would be,

$$\frac{x+y+z+\cdots}{n}$$

instead of p.

The departure of this from p may be written,

$$\delta p = \frac{x+y+z+\cdots}{n} - p$$

To estimate its likely value we have to average the results for a large number of rows. Since, however, δp is as often negative as positive, if we simply added up the columns the total would become nothing. We, therefore, square each departure before the addition. This has the effect of making all the values positive. Let us, therefore, try to work out the value of

$$\delta p^2 = \left(\frac{x+y+z+\cdots}{n} - p\right)^2$$

This is,

$$\left(\frac{x-p+y-p+z-p+\cdots}{n}\right)^2 \tag{1}$$

We have,

$$(x-p)^2 = x^2 - 2xp + p^2$$

Let us now add this quantity up for the first column. The value of x will be either 1 or 0, and since there are a large number, r, of rows, the value 1 will occur pr times. Thus when we add up the column we obtain for the term in x^2

$$\sum x^2 = pr$$

Similarly

$$\sum x = pr$$

Thus

$$\sum x^2 - \sum 2xp + \sum p^2 = pr - 2p^2r + p^2r$$
$$= p(1-p)r$$

We have also to consider terms such as

$$(x-p)(y-p)$$

which also occur in the expansion of the bracket in expression (1).

When we add up the columns, for a fraction p^2 of the rows $x = y = 1$. For these rows

$$(x-p)(y-p) = (1-p)^2$$

Thus these rows will contribute $p^2(1-p)^2r$ to the total.

For a fraction $p(1-p)$ of the rows $x=1$ and $y=0$. For these

$$(x-p)(y-p) = -p(1-p)$$

These rows will, therefore, contribute $-p^2(1-p)^2r$.

For another fraction $p(1-p)$ of the rows $x=0$ and $y=1$. These contribute to the total also, $-p^2(1-p)^2r$.

Finally for a fraction $(1-p)^2$ of the rows $x=0$ and $y=0$. For these

$$(x-p)(y-p) = p^2$$

and thus they contribute to the total, $p^2(1-p)^2r$.

Thus when we add up all the rows we find that

$$\sum(x-p)(y-p) = 0$$

The sum of the squares of the departures of all the rows will be

$$\sum(\delta p)^2 = \sum \left(\frac{x-p+y-p+z-p\cdots}{n^2}\right)^2$$
$$= \frac{np(1-p)r}{n^2}$$

The average value of this per row is

$$\frac{p(1-p)}{n}$$

The chance of the event not happening, $1-p$, is often written q. The root mean square value of the departure for the rows is therefore

$$\overline{\delta p} = \sqrt{\frac{pq}{n}} \qquad (2)$$

The probable value of the root mean square of the departure of the frequency in a run of n trials, therefore, varies inversely as the square root of the number of trials. To reduce its value to one-half means that four times the number of trials must be made.

When the number of trials becomes very large then the value of $\overline{\delta p}$ becomes small. This is the law of large numbers, but as we have assumed a frequency limit in our deduction of equation (2) this cannot be looked upon as a demonstration of the existence of such a limit. However, the theory shows how, on the basis of the assumption of the existence of a frequency limit, the likely deviation of the mean of a small sample differs from the mean of a very large run.

To see how this works in practice consider the tossing of a coin. Let the occurrence of a head score 1 and of a tail 0. The average value of any one throw will clearly be 1/2 if the coin is unbiased. Consider first single throws. Since any throw will be 1 or 0 and the mean value 1/2, each throw must differ from the mean by $\pm 1/2$. The root mean square value of the deviation will accordingly be 1/2. In the formula $p=q=1/2$ and hence the root mean square departure

$$\delta p = \sqrt{\frac{pq}{n}} = \sqrt{\frac{\frac{1}{2} \times \frac{1}{2}}{1}} = \frac{1}{2}$$

which is in agreement with the value just deduced.

Now in place of single throws consider series of four throws each. According to the formula the root mean square departure per throw should then be

$$\delta p = \sqrt{\frac{\frac{1}{2} \times \frac{1}{2}}{4}} = \frac{1}{4}$$

This can be checked as follows. In a run of four throws four heads can be thrown in one way only. Three heads and one tail can be thrown in four ways—the tail can occur either on the first, second, third or fourth throw. Two heads and two tails can be thrown in six ways. One head and three tails can be thrown in four ways, and four tails in one way. This is set out in Table 6.

In this table the various possibilities have been set out *in extenso*. A head is counted as 1, a tail as 0 and the mean consequently 1/2. Each possibility is as likely to occur as any other so that in a very large set of four tosses, each will occur in the same fraction. Thus the last column, which gives the square of the average deviation per term for each row, will contain each value in the proportion in which it would occur in a very long series of tosses. The mean value of the square of the average deviation per term will, therefore, correspond to that for a very long series. The net result of the calculation for the square root of the mean square of the average deviation per term, namely 1/4, is once again in agreement with the expression

$$\sqrt{\frac{p \cdot q}{pn}}.$$

TABLE 6

Throw	1	2	3	4	Average Deviation per Term	(Average Deviation per Term)^2
Series 1	H	H	H	H	1/2	1/4
2	H	H	H	T	1/4	1/16
3	H	H	T	H	1/4	1/16
4	H	T	H	H	1/4	1/16
5	T	H	H	H	1/4	1/16
6	H	H	T	T	0	0
7	H	T	H	T	0	0
8	T	H	H	T	0	0
9	T	H	T	H	0	0
10	T	T	H	H	0	0
11	H	T	T	H	0	0
12	T	T	T	H	−1/4	1/16
13	T	T	H	T	−1/4	1/16
14	T	H	T	T	−1/4	1/16
15	H	T	T	T	−1/4	1/16
16	T	T	T	T	−1/2	1/4

Total (Average Deviation)^2 .. 1
Mean (Average Deviation)^2 .. 1/16
Root Mean (Average Deviation)^2 .. 1/4

As the size of the sample increases, the probable value of the total square of the deviation for the whole sample, of course, will increase. Its root mean square value will be proportional to the square root of the number in the sample. The likely value of the average deviation per term, on the other hand, will decrease, and as the above discussion indicates, it will be inversely proportional to the square root of the number in the sample.

Part II

Chapter VIII

LOGICAL KNOWLEDGE

"Quod est ergo tempus? Si nemo ex me quaerat, scio. Si quaerenti explicare velim, nescio". Thus spoke Saint Augustine concerning time and he thereby described a situation similar to one in which we frequently find ourselves. If no-one asks us about a thing we feel we know all about it, but as soon as we start to explain it to one who asks, our ignorance becomes apparent. Logic aims at so systematising our thinking that we may become aware of what we may be said to know and what we do not know and so helping us to avoid inconsistencies. It deals with the process of inference and seeks to distinguish valid from invalid conclusions drawn from grounds already in our possession initially. It includes a systematic investigation into the conditions for valid thinking. Inference is an essential element in scientific thinking and, in consequence, logic is an important study for those engaging in science.

Inference may be of various kinds. For example, there is immediate inference from our sensations, as when we say that we are seeing a red colour. There is the inductive inference about which we have been speaking in Part I in which we reach a general conclusion on the basis of particular instances. There is also deductive inference in which a conclusion follows on the basis of given premises. Formal logic deals with the validity or otherwise of deductive inference, and is what we shall be occupied with in this chapter. It is called formal because it deals with the form of the argument which is used and not with the truth or falsity of what is asserted. It is upon the form of the argument that its validity depends. Thus formal logic does not determine whether or not conclusions are, in fact, true or false, but only whether or not they are justified by the given premises; whether, in fact, they *are* conclusions drawn from the initial data.

In logic we wish to disentangle the validity of the argument from the truth or otherwise of the premises. Argument can only start once we are agreed upon the premises or are prepared to accept them for the purposes of discourse. The relation of implication applies only between sentences. We must first agree upon sentences which, for one purpose or another, we take as premises for the argument. In logic what we are interested in is in finding out what necessarily follows if they are accepted. We thus separate certain difficulties, which as we shall see later on inhere in reaching agreement about experience, from the logic of the argument.

For a long period in the study of the subject attention was concentrated upon one form of deductive inference, known as the syllogism. Though it is generally recognised now to be not the only form which can possess validity, as was at one time supposed, it still remains, nevertheless, one valid form of deductive inference and it can serve to illustrate the essential features. Here we will limit ourselves to one or two fundamental considerations. For a fuller account of the syllogism reference must be made to a book on logic.

The syllogism is an argument in three steps. When set out in the usual order the first two of these statements are known as premisses and the third is the conclusion which follows from them. For example, we might say:

> "All gases obey Boyle's law.
> The inert gases are gases.
> Therefore, the inert gases obey Boyle's law."

This is a syllogism in the mood known as Barbara. (To aid the memory the valid forms of the syllogism were given names.) It is clearly a valid argument. If we accept the premisses given in the first two lines, we cannot avoid accepting the conclusion. The conclusion is, in fact, true. Moreover, such an argument could well have been actually used after the inert gases had just been discovered to be gases difficult to liquefy, which would be sufficient to distinguish them from vapours, easy to liquefy and which do not obey the law of Boyle. The question of interest from the point of view of logic, however, is not whether or not the conclusion is or is not true, or whether or not the argument was actually used by anyone, but solely whether or not the premisses justify the conclusion. In the present case the conclusion necessarily follows from the premisses and the argument is valid.

There has been some argument as to whether or not a valid syllogism, such as the above, could be constructed which was not, in effect, circular in its argument. It is the case that we could not be certain that the first premiss is true until we had tested all gases, the rare gases included, so that the conclusion merely repeats part of the statement in the first premiss. Clearly, however, the first premiss must be of the nature of a generalisation based upon limited information, if a syllogistic argument is to serve any purpose. We decide to accept it as a premiss in the knowledge that it is not completely certain. This uncertainty would, naturally, be carried over to the conclusion and, in practice, the conclusion would be put to the test of experiment as soon as possible. The uncertainty, however, is inherent in the premiss and not in the argument. The argument is free from uncertainty. Once the premisses are accepted, the conclusion is unavoidable.

We can see this more easily perhaps if we construct other similar syllogisms in which the truth and validity are varied. Suppose we said:

> "All gases obey Boyle's law.
> Alcohol vapour is a gas.
> Therefore, alcohol vapour obeys Boyle's law".

The conclusion is not true. It is untrue because one of the premisses is false. Alcohol vapour is not a gas in the same sense in which the term is used in the first premiss—namely, one of the so-called permanent gases. However, although the conclusion is false, the argument is a perfectly valid one. If the premisses are true, so also is the conclusion. Had alcohol vapour been a permanent gas it would have obeyed Boyle's law, which is one of the criteria for distinguishing a permanent gas. Incidentally, the element of tautology is again apparent. To be quite certain about the second premiss we would have actually to test the obedience of alcohol vapour to Boyle's law. Until we have done so our conclusion remains uncertain.

Suppose we altered the premiss in the first example and said:

> "Some gases obey Boyle's law.
> The rare gases are gases.
> Therefore, the rare gases obey Boyle's law".

We would arrive at a conclusion which is, in fact, true but we would have obtained it on the basis of an invalid argument. Because some gases obey Boyle's law and the rare gases are gases, it does not follow that the rare gases must obey Boyle's law. The rare gases might be included among those which do not obey the law. The argument is invalid but the conclusion is, nevertheless, true.

Had we constructed still another syllogism by selection from the premisses of the second and third as follows:

> "Some gases obey Boyle's law.
> Alcohol vapour is a gas.
> Therefore, alcohol vapour obeys Boyle's law",

we would arrive at a syllogism which was not only invalid but the conclusion to which was also untrue. The validity of the argument, which is what logic is concerned with, does not ensure the truth of the conclusion. This depends upon the truth of the premisses as well, so that logic, or at any rate formal logic, discusses only part of the problem of how to arrive at true conclusions. Nevertheless, it is an essential part, since unless our deduction is made correctly we cannot be sure of the truth of the conclusions even should the premisses be true. Logical considerations are directed towards achieving consistency in our thinking. Being isolated from the problem of ascertaining what is, in fact, actually the case, it can achieve a degree of certainty which cannot be attained in the sphere of observation and experiment. Once we know that our arguments are valid, attention can be concentrated upon the much more difficult question of the actual behaviour of the physical world, which is the object of science.

The form of the syllogistic argument can be set out graphically in the form of what are known as Euler's circles. For example, let us represent the class of all objects which obey Boyle's law by the large circle P in Fig. 7. Then we can represent the class of all gases by the

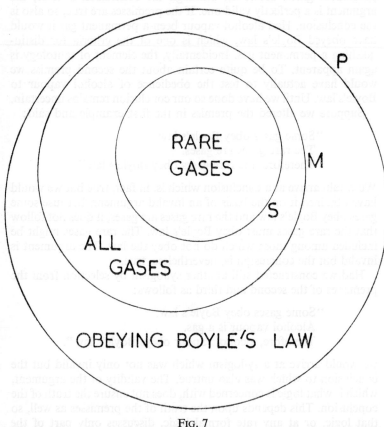

FIG. 7

circle M, which is entirely contained within P. The rare gases may be represented in turn by the circle S, contained within M, since it is a member of the class of gases. Thus S is contained within M and M is contained within P. It follows that S is contained within P. Another way of writing this syllogism would be

$$\text{All M is P}$$
$$\text{All S is M} \qquad (1)$$
$$\text{Therefore all S is P.}$$

The letters are those customarily employed. P stands for the major term, which is the term associated, in the premisses, with the predicate of the conclusion. S is the minor term which is associated in the premisses with the subject of the conclusion, and M is the middle term. The premiss containing the major term is known as the major premiss. The middle term is repeated in the two premisses and thus, in a sense, lies between the two extreme terms S and P. Syllogisms cast in the form given above are said to be in the first figure.

We need not pursue the question of the different figures and moods of the syllogism. Arguments of a similar nature to those we have considered can be formulated concerning classes which are excluded from other classes. These lead to negative statements. For example the syllogism

"No metals are electrical insulators.
Iron is a metal.
Therefore iron is not an electrical insulator",

is a valid argument and can be represented diagrammatically as in Fig. 8.

Other variations can easily be constructed. For our purpose, however, they would not add significantly to what we have found out already. This was directed to elucidating the nature of a logical argument. In considering any argument we have to look at two things, its validity on the one hand, and the truth of the premisses on the other.

We will now refer briefly to another distinction which it is useful to draw, to which these considerations lead us. This is the distinction between analytical and synthetic statements. Statements which are analytical are those which are necessarily true whatever the nature of the physical world. They are in the nature of conventions or definitions. They express the meaning which we agree to attribute to the terms we use. For example, if we consider the sentence "All fathers have children" or the sentence "All mammals suckle their young", it is immediately obvious that it would be pointless to test the truth

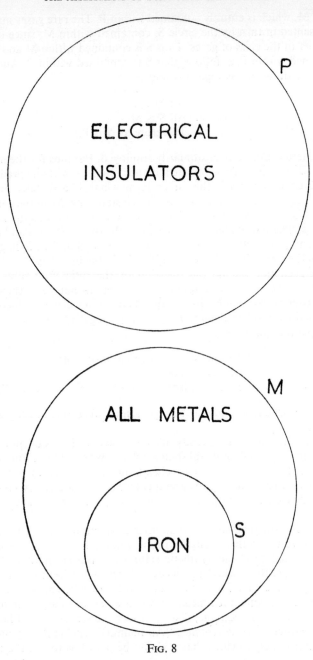

FIG. 8

of such statements by assembling a number of fathers and asking them if they had children, or by looking at a number of mammals and trying to find out if they suckled their young. A man who had no children could not be a father, and an animal which did not suckle its young could not be a mammal. The same is true of all definitions. We define the difference in electrostatic potential between two points to be the work per unit charge necessary to transport a small positive charge from one point to the other. This is also a convention. It would be pointless to attempt to verify the statement by measuring the work required in a number of practical cases. We have no other means of deciding the value of the potential difference, which is what our experiments would furnish as their result.

On the other hand, the necessity to be able to convert a definition into practical terms is essential if the definition is to be of any use, a fact which is sometimes overlooked in elementary textbooks. One does not alter the world of nature by sitting in an armchair and spinning definitions. The case of electrical potential difference, just mentioned, is a common example of this oversight. The difficulty arises because of what is often a praiseworthy attempt to shorten the approach to the subject through what was at one time a very lengthy discussion of electrostatics. In electrostatics a measure of potential difference is provided by the attracted disc electrometer and this, combined with a measurement of the ratio of the electro-static to the electromagnetic units, furnishes a measure of potential difference in the latter units. Almost all the elementary books which adopt such a shortened approach define the potential difference in terms of work per unit charge, as above. Many then employ volt-meters or potentiometers quite happily without showing how they measure the quantity which has just been defined. The definition shows that the potential difference is to be measured in joules per coulomb, in the practical system of units. In practice, standardising laboratories establish its value by means of an experiment depending upon electromagnetic induction, which is difficult in the elementary stages. It is not, of course, necessary to adopt an approach through electrostatics and, in a way, to do so is misleading. The readings given by voltmeters (including potentiometers among them, of course) do not, in fact, depend upon any measurement with an attracted disc electrometer or any other electrostatic instrument. Current electricity can well stand on its own feet. If it is made to do so, however, then another method of calibrating a voltage measuring instrument becomes imperative. The only method capable of being introduced in the early stages is by means of a heating experiment in which the value of the mechanical equivalent of heat is assumed.

The representation of electric and magnetic fields quantitatively by means of lines of force is a matter of convention, but the possibility of adopting it depends upon the fields following a law of inverse squares. A field which did not obey this law could not be represented quantitatively by continuous lines. It is sometimes suggested that the law of inverse squares is really obvious *a priori*, being a consequence of the three-dimensional nature of space. If, as is assumed in such demonstrations, the field can be represented quantitatively by continuous lines, the inverse square law indeed follows immediately, but the possibility of representing the field by continuous lines depends upon the validity of the law of inverse squares and the demonstration is circular. Sometimes the demonstration takes the form of proving Gauss' theorem on the basis of the same assumption. However, the necessity to demonstrate the validity of the law of inverse squares cannot be avoided. When the theory of magnetism is built up in terms of Amperian currents rather than magnetic poles, for which there is a good deal to be said, it is Ampère's law of action of current elements which then takes the place of the law of inverse squares for magnetism. For an elementary course in electricity to be logically satisfying, these points need emphasis.

If we assume the truth of our conclusions in forming one of the premises, the argument becomes circular and therefore invalid. This error is known as *petitio principii*, or alternatively as begging the question. For example, if we have calibrated our instrument for measuring potential difference by means of a heating experiment, assuming a value for the mechanical equivalent of heat, then clearly we cannot turn the same experiment round the other way and assuming our calibrations for potential difference, proceed to determine the value of the mechanical equivalent of heat electrically. If we did we would only arrive back again at the value we had assumed for the purpose of our calibration.

Questions are often begged because of the employment of ambiguous terms. Take, for example, the phrase, "the survival of the fittest". We possess in our minds some idea of what being fit means. We think of an active, muscular man, skilled as an athlete perhaps, or of a horse which has a healthy coat and is a good runner. The term is employed, however, in connection with the theory of evolution. Here its application is widely extended. For example, there is the case of the common weeds, which are thought to have evolved in comparatively recent times. How do we recognise fitness in a weed which enables it to survive? The term is employed in a different sense in such a case—in the sense, in fact, of being able to survive. The previous sense of fitness has disappeared and the argument has become circular and lost its point. The only way of distinguishing a fit from an unfit plant is that it has, in fact, survived. Some plants have succeeded in surviving while others have succumbed under prevailing conditions. It would be better to say that the former were better adapted to the conditions than the latter, a phrase which possesses fewer overtones. Even so when considering how a particular plant was better adapted than another we would simply be looking for factors which enable it to survive when the others perish. That is the meaning of the word adaptation.

Through the employment of terms in everyday use we lay ourselves open to the hazard of falling into this trap. Inventing a name like "heat" or "energy" or "electricity" we are prone to confuse what it represents with a material thing. We numb our senses to the necessity to ensure that it is, for example, conserved and to that extent, at least, behaves as a material thing. Faraday, who excelled in clear thinking (even though he called little on mathematics to help him in the process) once said, "The term current is so expressive in common language that when applied in the consideration of electrical phenomena we can hardly divest it sufficiently of its meaning or prevent the mind being prejudiced by it." We shall return to this point in a later chapter.

There is one other fault in argument to which elementary studies in science are particularly prone and that is special pleading—looking at only part of the evidence and suppressing that which tells against the case we are attempting to set out. It is by no means easy to avoid. In studying a scientific theory we naturally wish to understand the way in which it can be applied and the success it has in interpreting new phenomena. We thus almost inevitably concentrate upon achievement rather than upon shortcoming. A wrong impression can thus easily be acquired. In the ordinary affairs of life the same difficulty often arises. This is so readily recognised in a court of law that special provision is made to eliminate its effect. Two counsel are always empanelled, one to present one side of the case and the other the reverse. It was in illustration of this pitfall that Francis Bacon told the story of Diagorus, which we have recounted already in Chapter II. "Where are they painted who paid their vows and were drowned"? Only part of the evidence was presented to him and he was unable to form an unbiased judgment.

Students are rarely equipped with the knowledge which might enable them to raise awkward questions of this kind. All the phenomena cannot be studied at once. The theory has to be illustrated and the pupil exercised in its use. It is natural to concentrate upon those cases with which the theory can deal and to dismiss the remainder with a mere mention, if, indeed, they are mentioned at all. In this way a completely wrong impression may be created; the success of

7

science appears to be complete and nothing seems left requiring explanation.

As an example we might examine the emphasis which is placed upon the particulate nature of electricity. The concept of the electron as an electrical particle tends to be introduced in courses long before there is the slightest necessity to do so. The pros and cons of the picture are, in consequence, difficult to consider. An example of the almost deliberate suppression of contrary evidence is provided by the Hall effect. This effect, the deflection of an electric current by a magnetic field within a conductor, is basically very simple and capable of being understood at an early stage in the study of electricity. On a simple view it provides a means of distinguishing the sign of the carriers of the current inside the conductor. When it is put to the test, the elements which are conductors turn out to be almost equally divided among those which appear to have positive carriers and those with negative ones. Moreover, those with positive coefficients include such common metals as iron, zinc, tin and lead as well as cobalt, tungsten, molybdenum and tellurium, together with some eight or so others. The effect was discovered by Hall in 1877, but although an effect of this kind is to be expected on the elementary grounds of the electron theory of the conduction current, mention of it is extremely rare in elementary books. It is difficult to avoid the conclusion that this omission is due to the fact that the simple idea of an electric current as a flow of negative particles is not in accord with what is observed. The Hall effect is, in fact, only explicable if the electric current is given a wave rather than a particle interpretation.

Although this example may appear to be rather gross it is, nevertheless, a very difficult thing to prevent prejudice exerting any influence upon our dealings with observation. Satisfying explanations of physical phenomena are very difficult to come by and the search is exhausting. When we feel ourselves to be in possession of a true explanation there is a tendency to relax and to cease the search. Woodlice are found in the dark under stones and dead wood because they move very little in the dark and damp but do so vigorously in the light. In a similar manner there is a tendency to stick on a theory when we experience a strong feeling that it is correct. We cease to look around as attentively as we ought. An unconscious selection may well explain the result which Mendel recorded and which Fisher criticised. We accept without further thought those results which appear to agree with our theory and only examine further those which are not in line with it. Mendel recorded only one case in which he re-examined any of his results. That was one in which his results departed rather widely from what he expected to find.

Any such preference for verification as opposed to falsification is bound to weight the scales in favour of the theory. It is a pity that falsification is rarely as satisfying an achievement as substantiation. It deprives one of an explanation instead of providing it. It is destructive rather than constructive. Yet science can only operate through a process of elimination, and falsification must be the objective at which we should aim.

Chapter IX

MATHEMATICAL KNOWLEDGE

In these few chapters an attempt is being made to delineate the functions of various branches of knowledge. Any such delineation is, of course, dependent upon a number of perfectly arbitrary decisions. Human knowledge is compounded of a number of ingredients and it is convenient to consider each branch as being concerned with one or more of these. The demarcation between branches is not something which can be accomplished in a clear-cut manner, not open to question. Difference of opinion cannot be ruled out. It is not, however, of much importance to decide whether or not a particular branch embraces exclusively a given mode of thought. Rather the object is to enumerate and describe these different modes and in so doing it is convenient to ascribe each to a particular and recognised branch of study.

In thus describing the province of mathematics we shall start from the standpoint of pure mathematics and see what additions or modifications may be necessary to include applied mathematics within the boundaries of the subject. We shall discuss an attempt to reach some decision in particular concerning the demarcation between mathematics, on the one hand, and physics, on the other.

It was with pure mathematics in mind that the well-known toast was drunk—"Here's to the Higher Mathematics! May they never be of any use to anybody." In a limited way it describes the attitude of the pure mathematician, whose interest lies in the logical development of reasoning rather than in any practical value which may result from its conclusion. Taken in this sense, mathematics may be looked upon as a branch of logic. This is the view taken by those mathematicians who have been engaged in problems concerning the axiomatisation of the various departments of the subject and was the view in their *Principia Mathematica* by Russell and Whitehead.

The first example of such an axiomatic system to be worked out was, of couse, the geometry of Euclid. Euclid's geometry not only became the pattern for the rest of mathematics, but it also served to inspire much work in science, from Newton onwards. The whole of Euclid's geometry was deduced from five axioms and five postulates. The axioms were taken by Euclid to be propositions which were so obvious as not to stand in need of proof. The postulates were similarly thought to be deducible from simpler postulates, although they were not, like the axioms, self-obvious. The distinction between a postulate and an axiom is difficult to draw and serves little purpose. Both form the axiomatic basis from which the remainder of the geometry may be deduced. Euclid also attempted to define some of the primitive notions used in his geometry, such as that of a straight line, for example, but his definition as "a line which lies evenly with the points on itself" is of little help.

The science of geometry existed in large measure as a collection of empirical discoveries, long before Euclid's time which was around 300 B.C. It appears to have originated in Egypt, where it arose out of the necessity for the making of surveys after the annual flooding of the Nile. Euclid thus did not discover all or even most of his theorems by means of the deductive arguments which figure in his geometry. His achievement was rather that of unifying the whole of this branch of knowledge by showing how it might all be made to follow from a few simple propositions. His was, therefore, the first axiomatic system of a branch of mathematics to be developed, and for long it remainded the only one.

His system remained without rival for some 2,000 years, the axioms on which it was based being looked upon, throughout that period, as self-obvious propositions. Attempts were made at possible simplification of the axioms but no hint of any different point of view emerged throughout this time. In the course of time attention became directed towards one of Euclid's axioms, that known as the parallel axiom which is as follows. "If a straight line falling upon two coplanar straight lines makes the interior angles on the same side less than two right angles, the two straight lines, if produced indefinitely, must meet on that side on which are the angles less than two right angles". To many this appeared so far from being self-evident that it was felt that it ought to be deducible from the other axioms. All attempts to do this, however, failed. The problem joined that of the squaring of the circle, in a situation increasingly recognised to be hopeless.

In the course of these attempts to find a solution, many other propositions were found to be equivalent to Euclid's axiom. One of these, which became known as Playfair's axiom, was that two intersecting straight lines could not both be parallel to the same straight line, or what amounts to the same thing, through a given point one, and only one, parallel can be drawn to a given straight line. The sum of the angles of a triangle being equal to two right angles was shown also to be another equivalent, though hardly suitable for use as an axiom.

Many who have been brought up on Euclidean geometry or on

one of the variations used nowadays in schools, often, at first, find it difficult and, indeed may feel it absurd, to question these statements containing Euclid's axiom in one form or another. Some of them, if not all, appear to be quite obvious and impossible to doubt. Any who may still feel inclined in that direction should examine the geometry of figures drawn upon a spherical surface. Great circles drawn on the sphere correspond to straight lines on a plane surface. Great circles are the circles formed by the intersection of the sphere by planes passing through the centre. On the terrestrial globe lines of longitude are examples of great circles. They all intersect at the poles. Any pair of points on the surface of the sphere and at opposite ends of a diameter may be taken as poles through which a family of great circles may be drawn. On the other hand lines of latitude are not great circles. Except in the case of the equator their planes do not pass through the centre of the earth. Both straight lines in a plane and great circles on a sphere are paths which give the shortest distance between two points. If, on the sphere, we travel along any other path, such as along a line of latitude for example, the distance traversed is greater than along the great circle joining the two points, and any such path corresponds to a curved line in a plane.

Just as a plane triangle is formed by three straight lines in a plane, so a spherical triangle is formed on the surface of a sphere by three great circles. The sum of the angles of a spherical triangle is always greater than two right angles and the larger the triangle the more so is this the case. Take for example the spherical triangle formed by the equator and two lines of longitude such as PAB in Fig. 9. Two of the angles of the triangle are obviously right angles to start with, namely those at A and B. In addition there is the angle BPA. Now if we take the smaller triangle PA'B', in which the angle at A' equals the angle at B', we can see that both these angles are less than right angles and consequently the sum of the angles of the triangle PAB is greater than that of the angles of the triangle PA'B'. When the triangle PA'B' becomes very small it becomes approximately plane and thus the sum of the angles of a spherical triangle will approach 180° as the triangle gets smaller and smaller.

All great circles drawn on a sphere intersect. Thus if we are given a great circle on a sphere and a point on the surface outside the great circle, it is impossible to draw a second great circle through the point which does not intersect the first. To translate this condition into language corresponding to the plane it would amount to the statement that, given a straight line and a point outside it lying in the plane, then it is impossible to draw a second straight line through the point and parallel to the first. Parallel straight lines do not meet however far they may be produced. On a sphere they do not exist.

In so far as Euclid's geometry could be described as the science of measurement on the surface of the earth, it would be on a flat earth only that it would be valid. Over areas such that the curvature of the earth can no longer be neglected, it requires modification. We are,

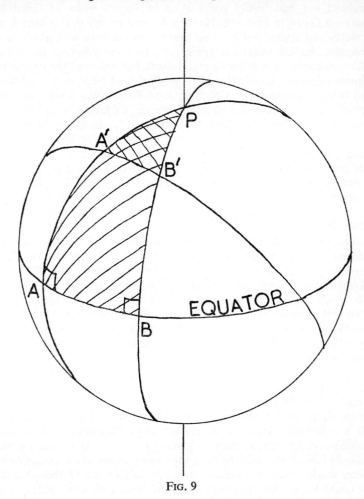

FIG. 9

of course, speaking more or less analogically. As far as plane geometry is concerned what we have said just above holds good. Euclid's geometry is, of course, three-dimensional and not two-dimensional, and comparison with spherical geometry can only be helpful as an analogy.

To return to the problem of Euclid's parallel axiom, we find this first analysed with any success by John Bolyai (1802–1860) in Hungary and Lobatchevsky (1793–1856) in Russia. John Bolyai's father, Wolfgang Bolyai (1776–1856) had taken an interest in the subject but had finally given it up in disgust when he failed to interest Gauss in his work. He then devoted his life to the writing of poetry and drama and it is said that on his death he was, at his own request, buried under an apple tree, to commemorate the three famous apples which, so he maintained, had changed the course of human destiny, namely those of Eve, Paris and Newton. In addition to being a mathematician his son, John Bolyai, was a musician, by profession a soldier, and equally eccentric. Of him it is said that he was once challenged to duels by thirteen of his brother officers. He accepted on condition that he should play a valse on his violin after each. According to the story he won all the duels and played each of the valses perfectly. Lobatchevsky, the son of poor parents and brought up by his mother from the age of seven when his father died, became professor and ultimately rector of the university of his native town of Kazan. He combined these offices with that of librarian of the university and also with that of a kind of political commissar under the Czar. Towards the end of his life he was deprived of his office. He became blind and his life's work, *Pangeometry*, was dictated. It was written in French and Russian. Lobatchevsky developed what is now known as hyperbolic geometry in which it is possible to draw more than one line through an external point parallel to a given straight line. Riemann (1826–1866) in Germany, worked out an elliptic geometry in which no such parallels exist. His geometry is analogous to spherical geometry and he introduced the concept of the curvature of space.

From our present point of view interest is centred round the consistency or otherwise of these various geometries. The initial motive for their invention had been to try to discover whether Euclid's parallel axiom could be deduced from his other axioms. If it is deducible from the others, as the parallel axiom solvers had endeavoured to show, then to assume that this axiom was untrue should lead to inconsistencies as the consequences of the assumption were worked out. No inconsistency was, in fact, found, though how it could be decided that the search had been sufficiently exhaustive remained a mystery until Beltrami (1835–1900) demonstrated that it is possible to represent Lobatchevsky's geometry upon a Euclidean surface. Because of this correspondence between the two geometries, if that of Euclid was self-consistent so also must be Lobatchevsky's. This, it is true, did not establish the absolute consistency of Lobatchevsky's geometry since both it and Euclid's might not be self-consistent together. Euclid's geometry had, for centuries, been accepted as perfectly self-consistent, however, and Beltrami's demonstration had placed them both on the same footing.

It is the question which arose as the result of the growth of the non-Euclidean geometries which is of importance to us at the moment. Their rise gave prominence to the question of what exactly was the status of Euclid's axioms. From being firmly established as self-obvious propositions they became reduced to the position of initial assumptions open to doubt. Geometry became the demonstration of the logical consequences entailed by the making of these assumptions, rather than a description of a space intuitively apprehended, as Kant had maintained. A severe re-examination of the logical basis of the whole of mathematics ensued.

For arithmetic Peano (1858–1932) developed an axiomatic system based upon five axioms and three "primitive terms", namely "number", "O", and "successor". The primitive terms were undefined and their meaning was to be obtained from the method of their employment. Frege (1848–1925) and Russell gave an interpretation of the primitive terms by means of statements about classes, enabling the whole of arithmetic to be set out as a branch of logic, employing no fundamental notions other than those like "class", "member of a class", "implies", which occur in logic. The statements of arithmetic, such as that $2 + 3 = 5$, became logically true and distinct from processes of physical addition. They certainly do not then mean, for example, that if I add a gallon of water to a gallon of alcohol, I shall obtain two gallons of the mixture. That we do not get two gallons of the mixture is an empirical fact. They do not even mean that if I have one bag containing two marbles and empty into it another bag containing three marbles I shall obtain a bag containing five marbles, though we know as an empirical fact that this is what will happen. They merely state that if I have three marbles at a particular time and that at the same time I also possess two other marbles, then altogether I must possess five marbles.

Mathematicians have shown that all the higher branches of mathematics require no other notions than those occurring in arithmetic. As a result many mathematicians, though not all, have become convinced that the whole of mathematics can be developed in terms of the methods of logic. The function of mathematics thus came to be looked upon as supplying the logical apparatus required for the quantitative thinking of science, for example. At the same time this view involved a divorce of the mathematics from the world of experience. Mathematics sets out the necessary consequences of any set of assumptions which must be accepted if the assumptions are accepted, for thinking to remain consistent. Thus the application of the mathematics to particular situations entails an additional enquiry. The mathematics, by itself, provides the logical calculus only and it needs to be interpreted before it can be applied. All its statements are conditional on the truth of the initial axioms. All mathematical statements are of the form, *if* so and so, (the axioms) then so and so, (the conclusions). Taken by themselves they are never a categorical assertion of the truth of the statements.

Even applied mathematics shares in this character, though the general view seems to be that it possesses an empirical content. However, applied mathematics is the investigation of bodies possessing postulated properties. The question of the occurrence or otherwise of such bodies in the world of experience then becomes a question lying outside the sphere of mathematics. The examination of the applicability of the axioms or assumed properties taken as the basis for the mathematics, and their logical consequences, to the world of experience belongs, on this view, to science. Such a line between the two types of investigation, the logical enquiry of the mathematicians, on the one hand, and the empirical enquiry of the scientists, on the other, can serve as a demarcation between the subjects. Mathematics is concerned with what *would* happen if...; science is concerned with what *does* happen.

Those who maintain that mathematics should be defined as what mathematicians do, are not likely to rest content with this demarcation. In spite of their toast, it is probably very rarely indeed that mathematicians investigate a purely mathematical problem without thought for occurrences in the world of experience. But mathematicians do many things besides thinking about mathematics. They go to bed, eat bacon and eggs for breakfast, clean the car and wash up. What has to be decided is what they are doing when they are doing mathematics, and to pursue a demarcation on the basis of the observed activities of mathematicians is not very helpful. However, as explained earlier, any solution to the problem of demarcation is necessarily arbitrary, and whether we call a particular activity mathematics or not is relatively unimportant, indeed trivial. What these investigations have shown is that the logico-mathematical thinking indulged in most by mathematicians, is an essential ingredient in human thought. We may take this mode of thought as the defining character of the subject. No-one wants to be a mathematician all the time and the incentive for some, if not indeed a large proportion, of the mathematics which is done, will always arise from the concrete problems thrown up by science. Nevertheless, the important function which only mathematics can fulfil is to codify knowledge obtained elsewhere and to show how it may be derived from a comparatively small number of postulates. Such a process helps both in remembering what has been discovered and in understanding it. By developing chains of indirect evidence it also contributes to the degree of credibility of hypotheses, as will be seen in the next chapter.

Chapter X

SCIENTIFIC KNOWLEDGE

Looked at in the way described in the previous chapter mathematics becomes immune to the doubts which are inevitably attached to empirical knowledge. It makes no statement about the real world but only about the consequences contingent upon the truth of the premisses from which it starts. In contrast with this, scientific knowledge is about the world of experience and is inseparably connected to a measure of uncertainty. Some of the difficulties associated with attempts to make statements about the physical world will be discussed in the later chapters. At the moment we note firstly, what is generally accepted, that all scientific measurement is subject to error and therefore can only be asserted, at most, as being approximately true. Everyone accepts the truth of this statement and pays at least lip service to the uncertain nature of scientific knowledge which results therefrom. However, although it is by no means the only source of uncertainty nor the most difficult problem to be solved, the uncertainty inherent in science is often very soon forgotten and in the pronouncements of many people, including among them scientists who ought to know better, scientific knowledge becomes credited with a degree of certainty to which it cannot attain. Some may feel that the degree of uncertainty may be made as small as desired by the taking of sufficient care. Some may feel that, although remaining uncertain, scientific knowledge still represents the best that can be achieved and is the surest form of any knowledge we may be said to possess.

Scientific argument has often been looked upon as generalisation. On the basis of a limited number of examples, a general statement is propounded. Alternatively, the confirmation of deductions from a hypothesis has been taken as establishing the hypothesis. The argument is of the form "If A then B. But B, therefore A". Neither argument is logically valid. This uncertainty inheres in the nature of scientific argument and would remain, even if the errors of experiment could be eliminated. The results of all scientific observations are, at best, a number of particular instances, never a general statement. Scientific observation cannot demonstrate the truth of a hypothetical general statement. This, of course, is the so-called "problem of induction" and we have already discussed one line of approach to solution in Part I, when we considered the theory of probability and Bayes' theorem.

Scientific knowledge is based upon the interpretation of evidence. Evidence is of two kinds—direct and indirect. Direct evidence for the truth of a general statement consists in instances of the truth of the statement. The evidence for Boyle's law is provided by examples of the measurement of the values of the pressure and volume of various quantities of different gases kept at constant temperatures, illustrating the law of reciprocal proportionality that exists between the two variables. Direct evidence supporting a hypothetical statement consists in the confirmation in particular cases of deductions made from the hypothesis.

The hypothesis or general statement may, in its turn, be deducible from other hypotheses or more general statements which can be supported on other grounds. When this is the case indirect evidence in favour of the hypothesis under examination is provided. Boyle's law for gases is deducible from the more general laws of the kinetic theory of gases. It thus receives some reinforcement from this source as well as contributing its own direct evidence to support the more general theory. No doubt, in the case of Boyle's law the evidence is preponderantly direct and only to a relatively small extent indirect through the kinetic theory of gases. On the other hand, the indirect evidence is relatively much more important in the case, say, of the osmotic pressure of substances in solution, and may become preponderant in cases where direct observation is difficult, as for example in determining the complete orbit of a new planet on the basis of the first few observations of its position. It is the value of indirect evidence which furnishes the incentive for the construction of hypothetico-deductive systems embracing a wide sweep of phenomena.

It is clear that the status of scientific theories varies. Some are well founded and comparatively difficult to doubt, whereas others contain a large hypothetical element and are much less secure. The growth of a scientific criticism, in which problems of the status of various scientific theories can be discussed, is much to be desired. This function should fall within the province of the philosophy of science, but so much of the philosophy of science is taken up with the discussion of what the scientific method is, that the other problem of detailed criticism tends to be neglected.

Two classes of scientific thinking can be distinguished. The first is that which is involved in the ordinary day to day work of the scientist. He is engaged in studying the phenomena practically, and in formulating working hypotheses to enable him to deal with the situation he finds, and to place it within his grasp and comprehension. An example of his procedure will be given later when the speculations of Lord Rutherford about the structure of the atomic nucleus are considered. Such thinking is creative. The systems which are evolved are invented and not discovered. Considerable call is made upon the imagination, and inspiration, rather than a plodding application of the strict rules of logic, is called for. It is the problem of how to justify the way in which science is able to arrive at its results in this manner that has engaged the attention of the philosophers working in this field ever since the initial synthesis of Newton started modern science in its career. This creative thinking is of the greatest importance and its philosophic examination throws light on the general problems of knowledge which it exemplifies. The problem of detailed criticism, however, in which one theory is compared with another and their relative strengths and credibilities assessed, is not covered by these investigations. Just as in the field of the arts, there is to be found a literary or artistic criticism, which is distinct from the general theory of aesthetics, so in the sciences there would appear to be a place for a more detailed type of criticism than flourishes at the moment. No doubt specialists working in particular fields are well enough aware of the limitations in the theories which they meet but there is little mechanism for making this publicly available.

In this connection it may well be argued that the place of the scientific critic should be occupied by the scientist himself and his colleagues engaged in the same field in which he works. Only those who are versed in the details of the field in question are in a position to form a judgment. This, no doubt, is true, at least, to a considerable extent. On the other hand it might be said that criticism based on this procedure is often not very likely to be illuminated to any marked degree by philosophical insight. Also scientific theories are read about and used by a wider circle than is actually engaged in their construction—by scientists working in other fields for example, as well as by the general public—and some serious attempt at assessment appears desirable.

As an example of the examination of a theory which is fundamental, widely used and well authenticated, let us consider briefly the status of the law of action of current elements in electricity. This law is the basis of the whole of the electrodynamics of steady currents. It was discovered by Ampère in about 1825. On what basis does this law rest today? It can hardly still remain based upon the same experiments by means of which Ampère substantiated the law originally, greatly improved though they were on experiments which preceded them. Ampère designed his experiments on the basis of null methods, in contrast to those of experimenters such as Biot and Savart, which were, in the main, simple direct measurements.

But Ampère himself had no other source for the electric current than the electric pile, and his experiments could hardly have been reliable to within much better than a few per cent. In present-day applications the validity of the law is assumed to be accurate to within a few parts per million. Furthermore, Ampère's experiments have never been repeated using improved techniques and certainly not to anything like the accuracy to which the law is assumed to conform.

Perhaps the basis today is indirect. There are, in fact, those who take this view. The law of action of current elements can be deduced from the inverse square law of electrostatic attraction combined with the special theory of relativity. While such considerations might well improve on the accuracy attainable in Ampère's day, it is, all the same, very difficult to assess the rather nebulous evidence available from this source. What is the evidence, independent of the magnetic fields set up by electric currents, upon which the special theory of relativity, in its turn, is based? How much of what is normally looked upon as the evidence for the theory of relativity is contributed by the movement of charged particles in magnetic fields, for the calculation of which Ampère's law has already been employed? If we omit the evidence provided by the movement of charged particles, to avoid circularity, what evidence remains? The evidence is undoubtedly very greatly reduced, although considerations such as the constancy of the velocity of light, based more or less indirectly upon the Michelson-Morley experiment, would remain. A little additional strength might also accrue from the general theory of relativity which, although not bearing directly upon the law immediately under consideration, is nevertheless based upon similar principles of relativity.

For purposes of the measurement of current we need to be able to rely upon Ampère's law to something like one part in a million. It is one of the most accurate measurements made in physics. There must be some one, or at most a limited number of experiments, to which we can turn to justify this reliance. As soon as an accurate experiment becomes available all the other less accurate ones on which we may have relied in the past, lose most of their significance. We see a countryman and ask him how far it is to the next village and he replies "Five miles". A postman arrives on the scene and he says "About three and a half miles". We tend then to disregard the evidence of the countryman. If then someone finds an ordnance survey map on the back seat of the car and we measure the distance and find it to be four miles and a few yards, we no longer bother ourselves with either of the rough estimates we had obtained so far. We do not simply rely upon an *omnium gatherum* of all the evidence that is available but are careful to weight it according to what we estimate its reliability to be. The total indirect evidence provided by a deductive system needs to be examined in a similar manner.

There is one point which, perhaps, might be raised at this juncture though it need not detain us for long. It is the question as to whether Ampère's law is, in fact, experimental at all. It might be that it is analytic in nature, being merely a disguised definition of what we agree to call the magnitude of an electric current. The law certainly does contain such an analytic element in it, but it is only of a minor nature. The proportionality of the magnetic field generated by an electric current to the magnitude of the current, or what leads to the same result though it is not quite the same thing, the proportionality of the force exerted by one circuit upon another carrying the same current, to the square of the current, is in fact analytical, and merely serves to define what we mean by the magnitude of the current. The remainder of the law, which determines how the magnetic field varies with the geometry of the circuit, is essentially a matter of observation.

The most accurate experiments involving the measurement of the force experienced by an electric circuit as the result of the proximity of another are undoubtedly those made with current balances in the various standardising laboratories of the world in order to establish units of electric current. They agree among themselves to something like one part in a hundred thousand. How far can they be used to justify the law of action employed in their operation? If all the balances that are employed were to be of exactly the same dimensions and geometry, agreement would be expected whatever law of action of current elements might have been employed in the theory of the measurements. It is only if the geometry of the current balances is sufficiently varied that any evidence concerning Ampère's law can be derived from this source. It would take us well beyond the limits of a book such as the present to discuss the variations in patterns of the various current balances which have been compared with each other in the course of establishing the unit of current, the ampere. Variation does, in fact, exist but it is not as large either in point of overall dimensions or in alterations in geometry, as would be desirable to establish Ampère's law with the desired accuracy. The purpose of the measurements has been principally to establish a unit for the measurement of current. The choice of a unit is, of course, a perfectly arbitrary matter, and identical current balances in the various countries, to fix the same conventional choice, would be all that is required. It could be made independently of any law of action of current elements. Such an arbitrary unit is actually legally valid in this country. The definition is as follows. "The ampere... being the current which flowing in and through the coils of wire forming part of the instrument labelled Board of Trade Ampere Standard verified 1894 and 1909, when on reversing the current in the fixed coils the change in the force exerted upon the suspended coil in its sighted position is exactly balanced by the force exerted by gravity in Teddington on the iridio-platinum weight marked A and forming part of the said instrument". A measurement of the force of gravity would clearly suffice to ensure that identical units were specified by identical current balances wherever they might be. Such a definition would clearly not be affected by the law of interaction of electric currents; indeed the theory of the instrument need not be worked out at all. It is only when it is desired to choose a unit which conforms to the theoretical definition that it is necessary to make use of the law of action.

It is not possible to pursue further this point here, but the discussion, as far as we have been able to carry it, would appear to indicate that experiments with current balances specially designed so as to vary the dimensions and geometry, would provide the best method of establishing Ampère's law to the accuracy which seems necessary. Whether this has been done in the course of standardisation experiments sufficiently rigorously to provide more than an arbitrarily chosen unit of current identical throughout the world, requires more investigation than we have been able to give it here.

Ampère's law of action enters into other electrical measurements of high accuracy, besides those with current balances. It is the basis, for example, for the determination of coefficients of induction. Upon these, in turn, depend the various methods for the determination of the Ohm and the Volt. It might be that variation in the types of inductances used for these measurements was greater than the variation in the design of current balances. Agreement in the value of the Ohm so obtained might provide stronger evidence for the truth of the law of action than can be furnished by the present types of current balance.

The explicit formulation of hypotheses which have been accepted implicitly is a valuable ingredient of the scientific method itself, as well as being an essential part of scientific criticism. By calling attention to assumptions which have been made without their having been thoroughly considered, or even made inadvertently, it can lead to further progress. The assumption that the wavelength of light was large enough to entail diffraction on a scale similar to that occurring in sound, delayed the consideration of the wave theory of light, to which delay the tremendous prestige enjoyed by Newton, who took the opposite view, contributed. The assumption that the waves were longitudinal, as in the case of sound, created difficulties for Huyghens

8

in connection with polarisation. In a similar manner, the assumption
of blending inheritance delayed the theory of evolution, the assumption that maladies were caused by bodily "tensions" which had to
be relieved, delayed progress in medicine and there is the classical
example of the naive assumption of the simultaneity of distant
events, first questioned by Einstein, which delayed the development of
electrical theory. As a possible example of the value of the examination of implied assumptions for purposes of criticism we might,
perhaps, consider the evidence for the expanding universe to be found
in the spectra of the distant nebulae. Lines which can be recognised
as being caused by elements existing on the earth can be identified
in the spectra of the distant nebulae, but they are displaced
towards the red. This displacement is interpreted as a Döppler
effect and is commonly accepted as providing evidence supporting
the theory of the expansion of the universe. In accepting this interpretation, however, a certain number of implicit assumptions are
involved. These distant nebulae are, in fact, thought to be very
distant and optical measurements on some as far away as 1,500
million light years or further have been made. One obvious assumption which is made in accepting the Döppler interpretation of the
phenomenon is that light is capable of travelling through space for
1,500 million years without change in wave-length. There is no
means of checking such an assumption. One cannot keep light in a
box for 1,500 million years and then take it out and examine it.
If it were not true then the Döppler theory would need drastic
alteration to say the least, if, indeed, it would still be maintained at
all. A second implicit assumption made in accepting this interpretation is that in the very distant parts of the universe—1,500
million light years away, a distance which the mind is practically
incapable of imagining—matter behaves *exactly* as it does on the
surface of the earth. That it might behave in a generally similar
manner might, perhaps, be not too difficult to concede, but that it
behaves in exactly the same manner as it does here, is an assumption
of a fact for which there is no evidence and which, if true, might
well be thought to be surprising. Another implicit assumption is,
of course, that matter 1,500 million years ago behaved exactly as it
does today. Again no test of such an assumption is possible. Evidently the evidence is, to a considerable extent, equivocal. Its
interpretation contains a large hypothetical element and is, therefore,
subject to considerable uncertainties. It is of interest to note, incidentally, that the first assumption concerning the transmission of
light through space without change of wave-length, has in fact been
challenged and the possibility of a different interpretation being given
to the whole phenomenon thus raised.

Science abuts on several other areas of intellectual activity. So far we have considered where a boundary may conveniently be drawn between science, on the one hand, and logic and mathematics, on the other. The demarcation between science and metaphysics has received considerable attention and also requires some discussion here. The mark by which we characterised science has been the nature of the evidence employed in the formulation of its pronouncements. The evidence concerned is obtained from experience without which no scientific statement can be made. Logic and mathematics deal with all worlds which it is possible to imagine and they are not limited by the facts of experience as we know them. Metaphysics also embraces questions upon which physical experience has little bearing.

There are those who would deny the reality of metaphysical knowledge. Such was the attitude of the logical positivists originating in the discussions of the Vienna Circle. This was a body of younger philosophers, at first loosely formed but which, after it had been active for some years, became formally organised under the title of the Verein Ernst Mach. The title was chosen advisedly. Ernst Mach, who had been professor of physics at the university of Vienna at the beginning of the century, took the view that physics should deal with the things which could actually be measured and eschew unobservable entities, the existence of which could never be demonstrated. The logical positivists wished to interpret physics in terms of observables. Similar views to those held by the Vienna Circle were put forward in this country by Professor Ayer in a little book entitled *Language, Truth and Logic* in 1936. These views became popular immediately after the War. Briefly they were that all knowledge was contained either in logic and mathematics, the statements of which were tautologically and therefore necessarily true, or in the natural sciences, the statements of which were capable of verification by experience. All other so-called knowledge was meaningless. To support this view meaning was defined as verifiability. In particular, metaphysical questions, upon which experience had no bearing, were meaningless and it was metaphysics against which the main fire was directed.

Clearly more than a tautological definition of meaning, identifying it with verifiability, was intended. If meaning meant no more than verifiability metaphysicians could have neglected the attack with complacency. Meaninglessness would signify nothing more than unverifiability and this would, no doubt, have been readily admitted at the outset. Unverifiability is a characteristic of metaphysical statements. Meaningless, however, was a word intentionally loaded. The term metaphysics became almost a term of abuse and those who gave their attention to it were thought of, by the logical positivists, as wasting their time.

The criterion of verifiability, however, in practice proved less simple to operate than had been supposed to begin with, and it had very soon to be weakened to mean the availability of evidence which had some bearing upon the statement, even though no clear-cut answer regarding its truth was provided. This, however, did not remove all the difficulties. Scientific verification, when it could be said to take place at all, did not, as a rule, verify a statement considered in isolation from all others. What were verified were, in fact, deductions and even so not deductions from a particular statement but from a whole nexus of interconnected ideas. When a statement was falsified there was often a wide choice of items to which the disagreement with experience could be assigned, any one of which could be modified so as to bring the theory back into agreement with experience once again. The attack, therefore, failed to be pressed home. There are signs that metaphysicians are again holding up their heads! Nevertheless the problem which the episode raises still remains in the background. The object of the logical positivists was to show that metaphysics was a waste of time and the verifiability definition of meaning was invented for this purpose. To express their point of view more moderately, it was that it is unreasonable to raise questions which cannot be answered by appeal to either logic or experience. This is a point of view. But it is equally valid to maintain that although metaphysical questions may not receive an answer, it is nevertheless important to realise that they can be asked. It is not a bad thing in using an instrument like the human mind, to attempt to appreciate some of its limitations.

Chapter XI

HISTORICAL KNOWLEDGE

In another direction the province of science marches with that of history. History deals with past events; so, in large measure, do geology and archaeology. Geology is certainly to be included among the sciences and archaeology at least makes use of scientific methods. The latter is also true of history to some extent, though many, if not most, historians would maintain that it possesses methods of its own which set it apart and differentiate it clearly from the natural sciences.

History deals with past events with which we can become acquainted only indirectly. Philosophers have questioned the possibility of justifying deductions as to past events from present evidence. Historians, like other men, must obtain their knowledge of the physical world, past as well as present, through the medium of their senses. Leaving aside the general problems (which face science as well as history) of our acquaintance with the physical world through the means of the senses, historians can, at best, have direct acquaintance only with existing evidence which is available at the present time. How can the inference to the unknown past be justified? How can it be shown not to be a mistake, as are dreams or hallucinations? Very similar problems are to be found in the sciences. Physicists infer the existence of unobserved, sub-microscopic entities in order to explain the macroscopic phenomena with which their measurements are directly concerned. Geologists infer the existence of past ages during which there occurred the vast accumulations of the sedimentary rocks which they observe.

But history, it is said, is not a "mere chronicle". It is more than a statement of the record of physical events which have occurred. To be history the reasons for past occurrences have to be elucidated. The causes of revolutions and wars and the objectives of foreign policies have to be discussed. For this purpose the historian has to "think himself back again into the period" he is studying. He has to make himself aware of the climate of opinion in which the actors in his scene played their parts. He has to understand their motives and intentions. He has to rethink the past. Because of the philosophical difficulties inherent in becoming directly acquainted with past thought, it has even been suggested that he has to recreate the same thoughts and actually to relive the past in an almost literal sense. The *same* thoughts which existed in the past have to be revived again in the mind of the historian. As a dramatic account of what the historian tries to do there is little harm in such a description. It can hardly be used, however, to justify the statement that the historian, by actually reviving past thinking in his own mind, has thereby direct acquaintance with it. The philosophical difficulty cannot be removed in this way. The thoughts with which the historian thus has direct contact are his own—the thoughts which he is thinking with his own, modern mind. What guarantee has he that the thoughts which he thinks he is rethinking, are in fact, those which actually occurred to the medieval barons or the Roman emperors as the case may be, who, no doubt, thought in a rather different way from that in which the modern historian thinks today, and even from the way the historian may think they thought?

Nevertheless the fact that the historian has to deal with human motives, actions and thoughts, is an important factor when one is attempting to distinguish his subject from the natural sciences. The removal of teleological arguments marked the beginnings of the era of modern science. Motives and desires are no longer attributed to inanimate objects. An explanation of the motion of the heavenly bodies by means of intelligences is no longer acceptable. Desires and motives remain only in the province of human beings. Geologists deal with the effects of the blind action which geophysical forces had in the past. Psychology, which also deals with human desires and thoughts, is in many ways a halfway house between history and science. The psychologist tries to codify the phenomena with which he deals by theories of a scientific nature, involving the putting forward and testing of hypotheses. For this purpose he may make use of experiment and measurement. He introduces the scientific method into the study of human behaviour.

Historical events are, in a sense, unique. They each occurred once and are never exactly repeated. Far from history repeating itself one can never, it has been said, step into the same stream twice. For that matter, the same could be said of any event that one cared to name, whether purely physical or humanly motivated. Events in the physical sciences are never exactly repeated. The cosmos is continually changing all the time and it is only because we judge some events to be irrelevant that certain events can be said to be repeated at all. Historical events, however, are compounded of so many factors which obviously bear at least some relevance to what has occurred that repetition, in the sense in which the term is employed in the sciences, is not possible. This entails the impossibility of experiment. Conditions cannot be varied at will and the results observed. The conditions which gave rise to an event in history, say a revolution or a war, are never exactly the same as those occurring in another case of the same general kind. The revolution in England in the seventeenth century, the French revolution of the eighteenth and the Russian revolution of the twentieth century, were all revolutions but the causes of each were different. The historian has to examine each case on its own merits. The men involved in each were what they were, imbued with those ambitions which appeared to them of importance, but untouched by others which, to later observers, might appear of greater value.

How then can cause and effect be said to work in history? That one event is the cause of another can only be said by virtue of a general rule—that events of the first kind are always followed by events of the second. If historical events are unique, where is the constant conjunction to be found to satisfy the demands of Hume? What, indeed, can be meant by historical explanation? Is there such a thing as historical explanation at all? Should history be driven to restrict itself to the "mere chronicle" of events?

One of the motivating objectives which the scientist has before him is that his explanations will enable predictions to be made. The future can be confidently assumed to be conformable to the past and a scientific study of events can secure for the worker a mastery over nature. If exceptions be made of men like Spengler and Toynbee, it can be said that the historian is actuated by no such motive. The exact conditions of the past never recur in the future. History never repeats itself. The object of the historian, it is said, is to describe past events, to discover the exact situations in which they appeared and the atmosphere of ambitions and cross-purposes which led up to them. The interest of the historian lies in the past. The future is unpredictable and must take care of itself.

Are then the methods of the historian totally different in kind from those of the scientist and is history, in other words, *sui generis*? History possesses its own distinguishing features but there is no call to make a mystery of them. Doubtless history calls for special gifts but they have much in common with those required by workers in other fields of thought. What is meant when it is said that the historian has to relive or rethink the past? It is a phrase which, if accepted as a figure of speech, describes very well what a historian has to do. How does he do it? Can he make any use of general statements, as the scientist does? What are his methods?

If the phrase "reliving the past" has any meaning it must be that the historian must try to imagine himself in the past and faced with the historical situation as it occurred at the time. He must try to imagine what would have been his own reactions had he been in the shoes of the various actors in his scene. In arriving at some ideas on this point he must equip himself with a knowledge of some kind, of the psychology of human action. He must know the sort of things which men do when they are faced by the sort of circumstances which occurred at the time and place in question. In part, at least, this can be based upon introspection and an appraisal of his own reactions in situations which bear some resemblance to what happened in the past. In part it will be based upon broader generalisations, such as that when the population is poor and oppressed and the government extravagant and foolish, revolutionary activities are likely to break out. In developing any historical explanation the thinking of the historian must necessarily be based upon the employment of generalisation, in a similar manner to that of the scientist.

It is not, however, the reaction of the historian himself to the set of conditions which occurred, which has to be imagined. The reactions of a man in modern times might well be fundamentally different from those of medieval or ancient times. It is the medieval man or the ancient who has to be studied. His ambitions, thoughts and actions have to be made familiar to the historian, who must feel confident that he could specify what the men who are the object of his study would do in given circumstances. It is this, more than anything else, which is conveyed by the phrase, reliving or re-thinking the past. A scientist cannot formulate a hypothesis until he is familiar with a range of phenomena within the field in which he is working. A historian cannot formulate a judgment about the period into which he is researching until he has made himself familiar with the actions and reactions of those who lived at that time. Nevertheless, the judgments at which the historian arrives are the judgments of a modern man and based upon material currently available.

The scientist proceeds from hypothesis or law at a low level to those at a higher, embracing a wider field. The historian proceeds similarly starting from his low level hypotheses about human behaviour. Often these are not explicitly expressed and thought of more as intuitions than hypotheses, but nevertheless their character is not otherwise very different. The scientist proceeds to test his hypotheses of higher level by using them to make predictions which can be verified or falsified. Here the historian must part company with him. As he seeks to advance beyond his initial position he cannot test his conjectures by means of predictions. In that sense a historical hypothesis does not "stick its neck out" and invite experimental checks, as does one in the field of science. The whole historical canvas has been completed and it can only be against that background that historical thought can be developed. For that reason we speak more often of historical judgment rather than of historical hypotheses. The historian has to endeavour to explain what particular concatenation of causes led to one particular state of affairs at one particular moment of time. Rarely is a crucial test conceivable. Historical explanations can only be checked against a judgment based upon the whole unfolding of history in general and upon familiarity with the period in question, in particular. Universal agreement, such as is achieved in the sciences, can rarely be hoped for; there are no clear-cut tests and differences of opinion can persist.

Broad generalisations can be made in history as in science, but the broader they are the less precise do they usually become. High level generalisations are of less value in history than in science. Though we might say, for example, that wars arise out of economic problems, such a generalisation could hardly be used to provide a certain prediction of the outbreak of war at a given time and place, nor could it be said that all wars have arisen in this way. The higher level hypotheses of science, on the other hand, are more precise than those at a lower level, since they specify more and are more readily open to falsification. The reverse tends to be the case in history. The broader the generalisation the less strongly is it held and the less do exceptions serve to refute it. Broad generalisations are, in fact, put forward, when they are put forward at all, as guides rather than laws. They possess an element of truth, as when it is said that discontent at home is often the precursor to a vigorous policy abroad, but there are many exceptions. Discontent at home might well get out of hand and lead to a change in government by revolution or otherwise.

To summarise this discussion we might say that while history shares many of the basic processes of thought with the sciences, it is distinguished from them in the first place by the fact that whereas scientific explanations tend to be mechanical in form, the ingredients in historical explanation are the nature of human conduct. While the scientist frames his explanations in terms of electrons, atoms, glacial ages, marine depositions and so forth—in terms, that is, of the mechanics of inanimate objects—the historian's explanation is couched in terms of intentions, plans, desires, conspiracies, ambitions and power, and the like—in terms, that is, of human motives and actions. The mechanics of electrons, atoms, etc., is drawn up on the analogy of the mechanics of particles observable by the senses and studied in routine laboratory operations or observed in the motion of the heavens. The characteristics of human behaviour assumed in historical studies are compounded of an intuitive psychology and a study of the "observed" reactions of the people of the period, the primary manifestation of which is to be found in the "mere chronicle" of the time. The main objective of science is to predict the future. The objective of history is to study the past and to evaluate and assess its course. Although the past has happened and is, therefore, not surrounded by the same uncertainty as is the future, nevertheless, the task of ascertaining exactly what the course of events in the past has been has many points of analogy with the scientific task of making predictions about the future. In the ultimate analysis both historian and scientist have only their own senses to rely upon and out of the experience which these provide both have to construct the worlds in which they work.

Chapter XII

ON LEARNING TO SEE

It is often quite difficult to realise that the art of seeing has to be learnt. The learning process takes place at such an early age that we possess no memory of it. At no time after birth have we been without the power of sight, though what we saw in the first few months of life can only be imagined.

Most living organisms are sensitive to light. This is true even of plants which possess no visual sense organs at all. Nevertheless, growth takes place in such a manner as to place the leaves in positions where they can receive light on their surfaces and thus where the vital process of photosynthesis can take place. Plant life indeed is centred on an intense struggle for the light. In some lowly animals, like hydra for example, there also appear to be no specialised sense organs connected with light, but if the animals are kept in an aquarium which is illuminated from one side only, they tend to collect on the illuminated side. Some jellyfish, related to hydra, possess primitive eyes, though it is unlikely that they do more than indicate the general level of illumination and assist the animal to remain the right way up. The earthworm is very sensitive to light and moves away from an illuminated area. It is only at night that earth-worms leave their burrows and wander about on the surface of the soil. The anterior end of the animal appears to be more sensitive to light than the rest but still there are no definite eyes.

Organised groups of light-sensitive cells, which might merit the name of eye, are found in the mollusca. The snail possesses a quite advanced type of eye. It consists of a little capsule with light-sensitive cells—the retina—at the back, and a large transparent mass which fills the rest of the cavity and serves as a lens. Bivalve molluscs possess a large number of eyes along the edge of the "mantle" which lines the shell. It is doubtful if any of these sense organs can enable their owners to recognise form, although there has been some debate on the point.

The arthropods, which include the insects, possess a highly developed sense of sight, but their conspicuous compound eyes are quite different in structure from the eyes of the vertebrates. The surface of the eye is divided into a large number of facets each of which is the outer end of a columnar unit. At the base of the columns

111

are light-sensitive cells connected by nerve fibres with the central nervous system of the animal. The body of the column is filled with transparent cells, acting as a lens to concentrate the light on to the sensitive retinal cells. The method in which the eye operates differs somewhat from one animal to another. In those insects with the clearest vision, such as the housefly, the honeybee, the hoverfly, etc., each column acts separately from its neighbours. The visual image is built up as a mosaic from the totality of the columns, which may

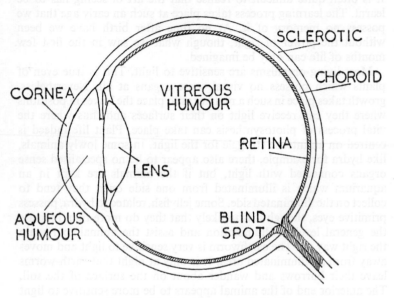

FIG. 10 *Horizontal section of the eye*

number some 2,000 or more in each eye. Excellent minute photographs have been taken using the eye of a beetle as a lens and there is no doubt that the compound eye of the insect is capable of providing the animal with excellent eyesight including, in some cases at least, colour vision.

The human eye consists of a hollow, more or less spherical chamber filled with a transparent jelly-like substance known as the vitreous humour. The outermost layer comprising the wall of the chamber is known as the sclerotic. It is visible from the front where it forms the white of the eye. It is continued across the front of the eye as a transparent section known as the cornea. Inside the sclerotic is a second layer known as the choroid. It contains a network of blood-vessels and is dark in colour. It is absent in the front of the eye, the opening forming the pupil. Its edges, surrounding the pupil, are coloured differently and form the iris. Below the cornea and in front of the iris is a watery fluid known as the aqueous humour. Behind the iris and supported by ligaments attached to muscles, lies the lens. This is a biconvex lens but it is not rigid. Its shape, and thus its power, can be altered slightly by the muscles attached to it. The innermost lining of the eye is the retina, the light-sensitive layer. It occurs only on the back inner surface and is missing on the front. Its structure is rather curious in that it appears to be built back to front. Thus the light-sensitive cells—the rods and cones—face away from the direction of the incident light. The nerve fibres which connect the sensitive cells to the brain lie on the surface towards the lens. Thus light has to penetrate this layer of nervous tissue before reaching the sensitive cells, and the nerves, in their turn, have to penetrate the retina in order to form a connection with the brain. The connection is made by means of the large optic nerve and where it penetrates the retina it gives rise to a blind spot. As the blind spots in each eye do not come at the same part of the visual field, they cause no difficulty and it requires a little experiment to demonstrate their presence, though it is very easy to do and the procedure is well known.

One particular area of the retina is more sensitive than the remainder and is known as the fovea centralis. Here the inside layers have been thinned out and only cones are present in the sensitive layer. The fovea centralis occurs at the centre of an area known as the yellow spot because of a slight yellow coloration of this part.

The eye works like a camera. An inverted image of external objects is thrown upon the retina, the cells of which are stimulated by the incident light. For clear vision it is essential that the image should be in focus. In a camera this is secured by moving the lens backwards or forwards as necessary, according to the distance of the object being photographed. The bony fishes adjust the focus of their eyes in the same way, but in the human eye focusing is accomplished by changing the shape of the lens by muscular effort. The focusing of the eye in this way is known as accommodation. Power of accommodation is lost in the elderly and the eye becomes the equivalent of a fixed focus camera. Extra lenses, in the form of spectacles, have then to be employed to alter the focus. If the eye is "normal" the focus becomes fixed on distant objects and glasses are required for reading. If the focus becomes fixed on objects nearby, glasses will be required for distant vision.

A number of defects are liable to be present in the eye. In short sight distant objects cannot be focused and in long sight the reverse is the case. Both defects are caused by the strength of the lens not matching the length of the eyeball and they are both easily corrected by means of spectacles. Astigmatism is caused by the lens of the eye possessing a cylindrical curvature in addition to its normal spherical curvature. Lines in different directions are thus focused differently. Like the other defects astigmatism can also be corrected by suitable spectacles which possess a cylindrical curvature to compensate that of the lens of the eye. Another not uncommon defect is colour blindness. This occurs in about two per cent of human males and in a very much smaller proportion of females. It is controlled by a recessive gene carried on the sex chromosome. Colour blindness thus occurs principally in men, who possess only one sex chromosome, so that the recessive character develops full effect. It is, however, transmitted to them by their mothers, who carry the gene but who nevertheless probably possess full colour vision themselves, since the effect of the recessive gene is masked by its fellow on the other sex chromosome. Colour blindness is of various kinds and degrees, the commonest being an inability to distinguish between red and green. A story is told that John Dalton put a red hunting coat down on the grass one day and was unable to find it. To a completely colour-blind man the world of colour must remain a completely closed book. All the same, it may be a long time before the defect is discovered, even by the colour-blind man himself. He learns to use the language of the normally sighted and distinguishes between terms such as red and green, which he hears his friends using, in terms of the subtle differences which he thinks he discovers in the objects discussed, often depending upon differences in brightness. There appears to be an inborn reluctance to admit any form of inferiority, even to oneself, and often the possibility of such a thing being the case does not occur to one at all. When it does a defence mechanism is put into operation and the defect is not admitted to anyone including the person himself. Some interpretation has to be put on the words employed by the people one meets and one just does the best one can without realising the deficiency.

The image formed on the retina is not perceived instantaneously nor does the impression disappear the moment stimulus is removed. It is on this persistence of vision that the cinematograph is based and which enables it to create the illusion of a continuously changing scene by means of a series of still pictures projected rapidly in succession. The eye can also be fatigued. If a bright image is kept on one part of the retina for a few seconds by staring fixedly at a certain point, then an "after image" can be seen when the eye is turned towards a dull plain surface. It is possible to fatigue one set of colour receptors separately from the others by looking fixedly at a bright coloured surface. The initial after image is seen in the colour complementary to that of the original object.

Blindness may occur from a number of different causes. When the optic nerve or retina fails to operate, little can be done to restore sight to the eye. Cataract, on the other hand, which is an opaque condition in the lens of the eye itself, can be treated by operation. Despite appearances the opacity is not on the surface and it is necessary for the lens of the eye to be removed. Spectacles are then worn to take its place. Without spectacles, of course, only a very blurred image indeed, arising from a pin-hole effect of the pupil, would be formed on the retina. Different spectacles are required for near and distant vision since there is no possibility of accommodation, but this does not give rise to more than the normal difficulties experienced with spectacles by those who have lost the power of accommodation. Almost all cases of operable blindness are the result of cataract. A certain degree of pre-operational vision exists in such cases, though it may amount to little more than an ability to distinguish between light and darkness. Some are able to estimate the distance of a bright light.

Cataract commonly develops late in life. When it does the operation restores the sight and results are immediate. The patient has learnt what it is to see and visual memories are sufficient to eliminate the necessity for any period of learning or relearning to see. The onset of cataract is marked by a gradual loss of the sensation of colour and the return of colour to the landscape gives particular joy. The sight of many of those who, in the Middle Ages, died in blindness, could have been restored had the operational technique been known.

Those who become blind comparatively late in life after the power of seeing has been fully developed, retain a memory of their sighted days and are able to understand the language of the normally sighted, as a result. They are not faced with any of the conceptual difficulties which confront those who were born blind or who became blind early in life. Helen Keller, the blind deaf mute, speaking of the difference between the blind and the sighted, said "In large measure we travel the same highways, read the same books, speak the same language, yet our experiences are different." It is in the case of the congenitally blind who have had their sight established by operation comparatively late in life, that the process of learning to see can best be studied.

Awareness of the environment will depend not only upon the efficiency of the optical arrangements of the eyes, but also upon the nervous mechanism, including the brain, upon which they act. The higher animals vary according to the sense upon which they place their main reliance. Fish living in deep, dark waters become equipped with barbels and other organs for sensing the bottom by touch. The bat relies upon sound used in a system of echo sounding, and for the dog the eye is subsidiary to the nose. It is extremely difficult to interest a dog in a picture or mirror image. On one occasion the author succeeded in getting his dog to bark at a large picture of a dog suddenly uncovered in his presence. However, as soon as the absence of smell was established all further interest in the picture subsided and it proved quite impossible to arouse it again.

The idea of space acquired by the blind man is no doubt very different from that of sighted persons. The blind often succeed to a remarkable extent in using other senses to replace sight and are able to find their way about and to perform certain duties by their means. A blind man may be able to find his way about his village by memorising the sounds encountered and acquiring a sense of the time taken by journeys in various directions. Passing a brick wall gives a different quality of reflected sound to what is heard when passing a hedge. Individual trees can be recognised and counted in the same manner, as anyone who has travelled in a motor car with the windows open can appreciate. The posts in a row of railings can also be recognised in the same way.

The space pictured by a blind man comes to him as the result of experiencing a series of events in time. He possesses no sense capable of presenting it to him as a single whole. To a large extent each situation has to be learnt afresh from the beginning. Having learnt his way about his house helps only in a minor way in finding the way about another. The exploration has to be carried out afresh. In this, of course, he does not differ fundamentally from the sighted person who has to explore each piece of new territory afresh also, but by his sense of sight the sighted is able to take in whole sections of it at a glance and his memory is stocked with images of very general applicability. For the blind the task is of a different order of dimension. For him it is essential to remember the finest detail in his diagnosis of his situation and the acuity with which some are able to do this is very remarkable. The slightest clue is seized upon and pressed into service. The ability of a certain blind man to recognise his friends by the sounds they made in breathing has been recorded "He recognised the presence of strangers in the house chiefly by the sense of hearing—for example, he could discriminate persons whom he knew by the sound of their respiration and he was at once cognisant of any breathing with which he was unfamiliar."*

Diderot said of his blind man "He has a surprising memory for

---

* Latta (1903 Glasgow), quoted by Von Senden, *Space and Sight*, p. 95. The man referred to was aged 30.

sounds, and can distinguish as many differences in voice as we can in faces. He finds in these an infinite number of delicate gradations which escape us because we have not the same interest in observing them.... The mutual aid our senses lend stands in the way of their perfection"* After her sight had been restored Joan "still judged people by their voices.... Whether smiles are sincere she determines by the smiler's voice."†

Although the blind place their main reliance upon different senses they nevertheless employ the language of the sighted. The absence of the possibility of a synoptic view of the space round them must make the idea of their environment which blind people obtain, very different from that obtained by the sighted. Yet it has to be described in the language of the sighted. Under such circumstances it is unsafe to assume that the terms used by each possess exactly the same meaning. This applies particularly to words describing shape. A sighted person is able to recognise a triangle or a sphere at a glance; the blind man has to run his fingers over them and count the number of angles in the first case or note their absence in the second. Much effort is required of him in the recognition of common objects. For this the texture of the surface, the sounds made when the objects are touched, even their taste when applied to the tongue, are of importance.

Apart from sound, the blind man is aware directly only of those objects which are in actual contact with his body. More distant space can be explored by movements of his hands and arms or other parts of his body. Space more distant still, such as that occupied by the furniture of the room, can be mapped by the number of steps required to be taken in a given direction before contact is achieved. It would be wrong, nevertheless, to attempt to generalise about the space perceived by blind men. The blind differ in ability and acuity, just as do the sighted. As a result of tactile and acoustic experience some may be able to construct a fairly elaborate picture of their surroundings in spite of their blindness. Others may be much more limited in their achievements.

The number of congenitally blind persons born who are capable of having their sight restored by surgical operation is now rapidly diminishing because of improved standards of hygiene. However, records, in varying degrees of detail, concerning the learning to see of those successfully operated upon, exist, dating from about the beginning of the eighteenth century. Extracts from those accounts of such cases which could be traced have been assembled in the monograph by M. von Senden, already quoted, and this has recently

* Diderot, Von Senden, loc. cit., p. 95.
† Getaz (1928 Lincoln, Nebraska) Von Senden, loc. cit. p. 95.

9

been translated into English. Although some of von Senden's views concerning the nature of the space perceived by the blind are open to serious doubt, nevertheless a large amount of valuable information about such cases has been assembled in this book and this is capable of providing considerable insight into the processes in which these people have been involved when faced with the task of learning to see. The examples quoted in this chapter are taken from von Senden's monograph.

In almost all the cases described, the operation was for the removal of cataract. Many of those operated on were of mature years and had been completely blind from birth. What residual sight was available to them amounted usually to little more than the ability to distinguish light from darkness and an awareness of the general direction of a source of bright light. Some had lost their sight at an early age and had lost all visual memory. Perhaps the most surprising thing about these cases is the length and difficulty of the process of learning to see. Some, indeed, became discouraged and never succeeded in the task. They were happy to relapse into blindness again and be relieved of the effort required of them if they were to master their new sense. After the removal of the cataract the patient finds himself in a highly uncongenial situation. From a world he knew he emerges into a *terra incognita*. He is unable to effect an immediate transference of his ideas of shape, for example, derived from tactual experience, to the new sense of sight. Various physical difficulties add to these obstacles. Often the eyes are unable to fix themselves upon an object, the image of which must therefore appear to move about the field of vision. Inability to direct both eyes towards the same object also occurs, though, as with squint, the patient learns ultimately to rely exclusively upon the impressions of one eye to the exclusion of the other.

Fischer (1888, Koenigsberg) reported upon his patient, an eight-year-old girl, as follows.

"Various things were now presented to her, which she must have known well from everyday life: an apple, a pear, plums, potatoes, an egg, bread, a knife, fork and spoon, a pencil, a box, a brush, a bottle, a watch, and her own doll. She knew none of these objects but naturally she hardly needed to touch them with her fingertips in order, once guided by her tactual recollections, to know at once what they were. Spectacles from $+9$ to $+16D$ had no effect on recognition, nor did the child indicate whether she saw any better with them. A large grey cat was set before her: she followed the animal's movements attentively, but did not know what to make of the visual impression and remained quiet until, on touching it, she cried out happily, 'The cat! The cat'!"

On the following day "the same kinds of fruit as yesterday were today put in her lap.... In vain! When shown the apple she fetches out a plum, which is six times smaller, or even the pear (which is half the size of the apple). She does not recognise a single one of the things shown to her yesterday."

An immediate concern of the congenitally blind, on the acquisition of sight, is the recognition of those common objects with which they come into contact. This has already been among their principal preoccupations when blind. As soon as they see, colour is among the first impressions remarked upon. This occurs in the initial period of great expectations immediately following the operation. It is soon found, however, that colours do not suffice, too many objects possess the same or nearly the same colour. It then becomes recognised that an intensive effort to learn is called for from them. At this stage a period of disillusionment and depression not infrequently sets in. What was expected to be a great gift turns out to necessitate a laborious process of learning. It by no means infrequently occurs that after the patient has made a few systematic attempts to practise his vision and has found, in doing so, how difficult it is to master the ideas of shape, his former condition of blindness appears preferable to him. Before he had his sight given to him he lived in a blessed state of peace, secure in the assistance provided so generously by his fellows. Now, no longer able to look to them for help, he has to master his own new sense and make his own way in the world unaided.

Moreover, he becomes aware that his blindness has resulted in a mental backwardness that will put him at a disadvantage compared with his fellows. Combined with this sense of his own shortcomings is often a hypersensitivity. "Things were quite all right when I could not see: why do you pester me with something that is none of my concern?"

Mesmer records of one of his patients: "In her ill humour she once complained to her father 'How comes it that I now find myself less happy than before? Everything that I see causes me a disagreeable emotion. Oh, I was much more at ease in my blindness!' The father consoled his daughter with the thought that her present agitation was solely due to the sensation of strangeness in the sphere she was now moving in. The new situation she found herself plunged into by the recovery of her sight must necessarily awaken in her an uneasiness never felt before. She would, however, become as calm and contented as others, as soon as she had grown accustomed to seeing. 'I am glad to hear it,' she replied, 'for if I were always to feel such uneasiness as I do at present at the sight of new things I would sooner return on the spot to my former blindness.' This in fact, she did do for after a time she again went blind."

Beer (1783–1813, 14 cases, Vienna) wrote, "Among the most remarkable psychological phenomena presented to my observation in all the patients so far operated upon, is the rapid and complete loss of that striking and wonderful serenity which is characteristic only of those who have never yet seen; for hardly are the first lively sallies of their curiosity satisfied after the operation, than already they evince this striking transformation in their attitude. Gloomy and reserved, they now shun for a time the society of others, which was so indispensable to them while they were blind that they lamented every moment they were obliged to spend without it."

In learning to use their sight the processes similar to those already employed during blindness occur naturally to the newly sighted. Initially he finds he is unable to grasp the shape of a large surface and finds he has to traverse the outlines with his eye in a similar manner to the way in which he used to run his fingers over the object to feel its shape. In this process texture, which is one of the main distinguishing features for the blind, is now of only very limited importance. Furthermore, in blindness actual contact had to be obtained with an object before it could be sensed. Some patients tended to transfer this condition to seeing where it was no longer appropriate. The blind often have difficulty in convincing themselves that a sense, which they do not possess, which presents the totality of the environment to the person, is at the disposal of the sighted. One of them described how "In order to satisfy my doubt, I had the idea of trying a strange experiment. One morning I again put on a dress which I had not worn for some time, because I had been growing so rapidly then from month to month, and thus attired I suddenly showed myself at the door of the anteroom in which my governess was already working at the window. I stood listening. 'Good heavens, Lucy', she said, 'why have you put on that old dress that only reaches to your knees'? I merely uttered a few idle words and withdrew. This was enough to convince me that without laying a hand upon me, Martha had immediately been able to recognise that I had again put on the dress that was too short. So this was seeing."

"The first thing I showed her" said Gayet (1884 Lyons) of his case, "was a candle flame, which she certainly claimed to recognise, though it inspired her with considerable fear. This was quite understandable, since up to now 'fire' as she called it, had appeared inseparably bound up with the harm it can do, and because she had only been acquainted with it till now through tactual sensation, without having any notion of distance".

In testing patients to ascertain what they can recognise visually it is necessary to be most careful to exclude all other clues which might help them to answer. A case reported by Grafé (1891, Namur) well illustrates the difficulty in doing this.

"When the Lady Superior showed him the large rosary that she kept at her girdle, and asked him what it was, he immediately replied 'That's a rosary'. When she seemed surprised that he could name an object so exactly on seeing it for the first time, he added that the noise made by the object when it was held out to him had reminded him of a noise to which his ear was accustomed, and which had long been associated, through other rosaries, with sensations of touch and manipulation".

It seems clear from all these accounts that the art of seeing has to be acquired. It is not accomplished by intuition alone, if indeed intuition plays any significant part at all in the process. In particular we do not appear to be provided with any *a priori* notions of space. The notion of space is a scheme whereby the experiences of sight can be correlated with one another and with those derived from other senses. The ideas of space possessed by the blind differ in character from those of the sighted. The ideas of shape which the blind acquire are much more limited than those developed by those who can see. The gift of sight is not a gift which can be acquired without effort. Learning to see is a task demanding much application. If left to a late age it is by no means an easy one and there are many pitfalls and discouragements. It resembles the learning of a foreign language and requires a similar degree of concentration.

Chapter XIII

PERCEPTION

"And did you see the dead man on Tryfan?" asked the Welshman of his friend who had just returned from a trip into the mountains. His friend blanched somewhat at the thought of a grisly sight but answered "No". However, there had been no dead man on Tryfan that morning. What the Welshman's friend had failed to see was that from a certain angle the summit of Tryfan has the outline of a man lying on his back, apparently dead. Only those with eyes to see would observe the fact at all.

FIG. 11 *The Invisible Man.*
(After H. B. Porter in
The American Journal of Psychology,
Vol. 67, p. 550, 1954)

The well-known picture called the "Invisible Man" contains a picture of a man, benevolent in appearance, whom most people find difficulty in seeing when they meet the picture for the first time. An artist, however, to whom the picture was shown, asked immediately, "Why is it called the invisible man?" To one possessing a

PLATE II *The summit of Trÿfan*

PLATE III *Pictures in the fire*

practised eye and used to interpreting drawings which leave much to the imagination, there appeared to be no difficulty at all. Once having seen the man it is hardly ever possible to lose him again and fail to pick him out on subsequent occasions. He stands out immediately.

All are familiar with the man in the moon—a somewhat indifferent interpretation of the markings on the moon—but few have noticed the lady in the moon. She is a rather elegant lady, in point of fact, and much more worth looking at than the familiar man! The list can be added to almost indefinitely. Pictures in the fire, statues by Henry Moore, modern paintings, all demand an effort from the imagination. In all these cases it is clear enough that seeing, like beauty, lies in the mind of the beholder, and is not simply an affair of the eyes alone. It can hardly be disputed that what is seen can have no material existence in the ordinary meaning of the term.

The eyes, too, are readily deceived. Illusions, ranging from images in mirrors, distortions caused by the refraction of light, to the well-known cases where judgment of equality of length, area or height can be distorted by the addition of extraneous lines to a picture, are too well known to need comment. A few have been assembled in Figs. 12 and 12a. These illusions are of two kinds. In the case of reflections and refractions (such as in Pepper's ghost for example) the image on the retina corresponds fairly accurately to what is seen. The illusion is produced by the actual formation of a physical image somewhere in space. It is through comparatively sophisticated experience that what is seen is known to be illusory. A kitten can be deceived by a mirror for a long time. On the other hand, in the case of the optical illusions in the form of drawings on paper, such as those in Fig. 12, the image on the retina reproduces the drawings quite exactly but what is seen does not correspond to it. Lines are seen to be longer or shorter than they really are. The eye, considered as a piece of physical apparatus, as a camera in fact, continues to work perfectly. It is the mechanism involved in the interpretation of the significance of the retinal image that is at fault.

We are also capable of seeing things that are not there at all and which have recorded no image on the retina. The man in delirium tremens sees his pink elephants. Ordinary people, like ourselves, however, who are not in any such extreme condition, can see a conjuror pass an object from one hand to the other, only to stand amazed as he opens his hand and shows us that it is not there. We thought we saw the object pass but, in fact, we did not do so. The opposite is also the case on other occasions, when we fail to see things which are before us and staring us in the face, though hardly deserving comment since it is so common. We cannot give attention to everything at once and on these occasions it is never directed to the object of which, perhaps, we are in search.

When we dream we see things which we have no hesitation in saying were unreal when we wake up. Whether our sense organs are stimulated in some manner when we dream is difficult to determine, but our minds appear to be provided with exactly the same sort of information as if they were. How we distinguish between the

FIG. 12. *An optical illusion.*

All the balls in the picture are of the same size though that near the goal seems to be larger than the others.

states of dreaming and waking, is not easy to decide. When we are awake we have no difficulty, as a rule, in deciding upon the question of whether we are dreaming or not. If we have concussion or have taken certain drugs, then even the real world takes on a rather unreal appearance and we are not so sure whether we may be dreaming or not. But when we dream we often feel as if we are awake. It can only be the consistency with which the behaviour of the things which we observe in dreams, corresponds or fails to correspond with what we are familiar with during our waking hours as the ordinary behaviour of the entities we are seeing, which can furnish any criterion.

It is clear that we do not see with the eyes alone. Yet, in spite of this, no one has the slightest hesitation in affirming that he can see a chair or other common object at which he is looking. If it is pointed out that he must be actually interpreting sensations arising from the images on the retinas of his eyes and that he is not, himself, in contact with the chair in any strict sense, he is tempted to reply that

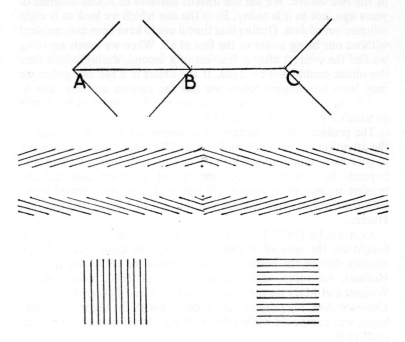

FIG. 12a. *Further optical illusions.*

The line AB is actually longer than BC though it appears shorter. The boundaries of the hatched areas have parallel sides. Both the lower shaded figures are squares.

he can also become aware of the chair by means of other senses in addition, in particular through the sense of touch. But this fails to remove the objection that he is not in actual contact with the chair himself but that he can only be interpreting sensations arising from a stimulus he is receiving, sensations of resistance to movement for example, or of pressure and texture. That his sensation is caused by an external stimulus at all is an assumption. Moreover it is just as possible to have spurious sensations of touch as it is to have them of sight. The man whose leg has been amputated feels pain in the toes he no longer possesses. There is also the difficulty that what we see or hear or feel, are not present happenings but the result of happenings in the past. Not only do light and sound take time to travel but so do the nervous impulses from our sense organs. The thud of the distant pile driver which we hear may well not be the sound of the impact that we see at the same time. It can easily be of the one before. We see the distant universe as it was millions of years ago, not as it is today. Even the sun which we look at is eight minutes out of date. During that time it could have been extinguished without our being aware of the fact at all. When we touch anything we feel the contact after a fraction of a second, during which time the object could have changed. If the object is a red hot poker we may burn our fingers before we feel the contact and are able to withdraw. The reactions of a snail are much slower and the world to which it can react has passed longer into history.

The problem of the perception of common objects has occupied the attention of philosophers for over 250 years, though in essence it goes back much longer than this—to the theories of Plato and beyond. Its history has become almost commonplace and the briefest account of its course will suffice. The modern period starts with the theories of knowledge put forward by Locke, Berkeley and Hume.

John Locke (1632–1704), the son of a Puritan father who had fought on the side of Parliament during the Civil War, left the country during the period of Tory reaction in 1683, and lived in Holland, returning with the revolution of 1688, which placed William and Mary on the throne. Locke's *Essay Concerning Human Understanding*, his principal work dealing with the theory of knowledge, was composed while he was abroad, but it was not published until 1690.

Locke's doctrine is that all knowledge is derived from experience, that is, the doctrine known as Empiricism, which he can claim to have initiated. "Let us then suppose the mind to be, as we say, white paper, void of all characters, without any ideas; how comes it to be furnished? Whence comes it by that vast store, which the busy boundless fancy of man has printed on it with an almost endless variety? Whence has it all the materials of reason and knowledge? To this I answer in one word, from experience: in that all our knowledge is founded, and from that it ultimately derives itself." (Book II, Chap. I, Sec. 2). To those of us who have had a scientific upbringing this may seem very obvious but in Locke's day it was a new idea. The doctrine, unavoidable as it may appear, nevertheless leads to immediate difficulty. It is, of course, far from obvious and, indeed, may well be wrong. How do we, in fact, acquire knowledge of the external world—the problem with which our introductory examination of perception brought us into contact? It is the problem or series of problems, posed by the sceptics, and we meet them again and again in various situations. First, how do we effect the transition from the data of the senses to common objects? Granting a solution to this, how do we pass from the observed behaviour of others to the existence of other minds? Again, how, given common objects, can we establish the existence of those scientific entities which transcend the senses? How, given a situation in the present, can we infer the past?

Locke proffers no solution to these problems. Indeed he gives little evidence that he is aware of them. Instead he sticks to common sense. The external world he takes for granted. He puts forward a doctrine of primary and secondary qualities. Primary qualities inhere in the object itself. They are solidity, extension, figure, motion or rest, and number. Secondary qualities, on the other hand, exist only in the mind of the observer. They include tastes, smells, colours and sounds. Tastes depend upon the organs of taste, smells upon the nose and without the eyes and the ears colours and sounds would not exist.

Whatever may be thought about this division of properties, Locke's idea of distinguishing between primary and secondary qualities has borne enormous fruit. His position was, in the course of time, taken as the basis for physics. The physical world come to be looked upon as being composed of particles possessing only the primary qualities of Locke—position, motion, rest, etc. Heat, light, sound, electricity and magnetism were accounted for by the movement of the particles. It is true that after the disappearance of the corpuscular theory of light, the elastic solid theory of the basis of light waves ran into certain difficulties, but the situation was not materially altered by the substitution of fields for the elastic solid. There still remained two categories of properties, the primary which are associated with the ultimate constituents of the physical world, and the secondary properties arising through the stimulation of our organs of sense.

What reasons can Locke put forward to show that sensations have causes, that these causes lie in an external world and that the sense impressions of which we are conscious, in some way resemble objects in the external world, so that we may obtain knowledge of that world from the impressions we receive? This is a problem which Locke's empiricism raises immediately, which he does nothing to solve and which, in fact, has defeated philosophy to the present time. Empiricism appeared to possess compelling attraction, especially in this country, in spite of its being in conflict with this difficulty. It has been the standby of much of British philosophy since the time of Locke. Common sense still has its champions. Could it be that common sense is wrong?

Berkeley (1685–1753), who became Bishop of Cloyne in 1734, challenged Locke's views directly. He believed, in common with many who have come on the scene at a much later date, that philosophers had got themselves into a muddle through the misuse of language. He felt that the solution of the difficulty was simple and that he had found it. Philosophers "first raise a dust and then complain we cannot see," he said.

Berkeley first points out that Locke's distinction between primary and secondary qualities cannot be maintained. Both are in fact mental concepts. "It is indeed an opinion strongly prevailing amongst men, that houses, mountains, rivers and in a word all sensible objects have an existence, natural or real, distinct from their being perceived by the understanding. But with how great an assurance and acquiescence so ever this principle may be entertained in the world: yet whoever shall find in his heart to call it in question may, if I mistake not, perceive it to involve a manifest contradiction. For what are the fore-mentioned objects but the things we perceive by sense, and what, I pray you, do we perceive besides our own ideas or sensations, and is it not plainly repugnant that any one of these or any combination of them should exist unperceiv'd?" (*Principles of Human Knowledge*, Pt. I, Sec. 4.) "In short, tho' there were external bodies, 'tis impossible we should ever come to know it: and if there were not, we might have the very same reasons to think that there were that we have now. Suppose, what no one can deny possible an intelligence without the help of external bodies to be affected with the same train of sensations or ideas that you are, imprinted in the same order and with like vividness in his mind. I ask whether that intelligence hath not all the reason to believe the existence of corporeal substances, represented by his ideas, and exciting them in his mind, that you can possibly have for believing the same thing". (loc. cit. Sec. 20).

Berkeley's solution to the problem of existence is that things are in the mind. This, he points out, renders them none the less real. "In the sense here given of *reality*, 'tis evident that every vegetable, star, mineral, and in general each part of the mundane system, is as much a *real being* by our principles as by any other." (loc. cit. Sec. 36). What are perceived are ideas. These are not under the control of the will. But it then seems to follow that things exist only when perceived. "*Esse* is *percipi*." To get over the difficulty of things springing into and out of existence according as they are perceived or not, Berkeley adds that God is always present and that unperceived objects are ideas in the mind of God. In this Berkeley feels that he has found the strongest evidence for the existence of God. His philosophical position is accurately described by the limericks:

> There once was a man who said, "God
> Must think it exceedingly odd
> If he finds that this tree
> Continues to be
> When there's no one about in the Quad".

> Dear Sir,
>   Your astonishment's odd;
> *I* am always about in the Quad,
> And that's why the tree
> Will continue to be,
> Since observed by
>   Yours faithfully,
>   God.

It was this notion of ideas in the mind of God that Berkeley thought provided the solution to all the difficulties and laid the dust raised by the philosophers. It was capable of explaining the whole "choir of heaven and furniture of the earth". His theory, however, has not lasted. Soon after putting it forward Berkeley turned his attention to the virtues of tar water and nothing further of any importance ever came from his pen. However, what does remain of importance, and what indeed is still unanswered, is his questioning of Locke's distinction between primary and secondary qualities. After Berkeley this distinction became no longer tenable.

David Hume (1711–1776), whose sceptical views we have already met in Chapter III, was the younger son of the laird of Ninewells in Berwickshire. He was brought up by his mother, his father having died when he was three years old. His main interests were literary. At the age of twenty-three he tried making for himself a commercial career with a merchant in Bristol but quickly gave it up and went to live in France from 1734 to 1737, with the object of continuing his studies. He lived at La Flèche in Anjou, near the Jesuit College where Descartes had been educated a hundred years earlier. Here he wrote his first and most important philosophical work, his *Treatise of Human Nature*. It was as a historian and an essayist that he was best known during his life-time, but this part of his reputation has not survived. His *Treatise of Human Nature* unfortunately "fell" as he said, "dead born from the press". It is, however, for his Treatise that he is now remembered, his other works being considered as of small importance. He appears to have been of a genial nature, well liked by his circle of friends, among whom, in spite of his anti-religious views, he numbered several clergy of the Church of Scotland. His Treatise was divided into three volumes; the first was on the theory of knowledge, the next on psychology and the third on morals. To direct attention to the Treatise he wrote, after its initial failure to attract attention but before the appearance of the third volume, an abstract as though from the pen of a favourable critic. Finally he produced a drastically revised version under the title of *An Enquiry Concerning Human Understanding* which watered down his original thesis, in an effort to make it more palatable. Nevertheless, its conclusions retained some air of ruthlessness.

"When we run over our libraries, persuaded of these principles, what havoc must we make? If we take in our hand any volume of divinity or school metaphysics for instance; let us ask *does it contain any abstract reasoning concerning quantity or number?* No. *Does it contain any experimental reasoning concerning matter of fact and existence?* No. Commit it then to the flames, for it can contain nothing but sophistry and illusion."

Hume's contribution to the theory of knowledge was to carry the ideas of Locke and Berkeley to their logical conclusion. In doing this he succeeded in destroying the basis of all reasoning and arrived at the most extreme form of scepticism. Ever since he wrote his Treatise it has been the desire of philosophers to refute him but no refutation has so far been evolved which has any prospect of success. While Hume's thesis remains unacceptable to anyone wishing to base his views upon reason it is, at the same time, irrefutable. Hume has thus placed us in a very difficult position. We cannot renounce reason and at the same time we cannot advance any reasons at all why it should be reliable!

Hume differentiated between knowledge based on simple direct observation, on logic or mathematics, and that of all other forms. The last were open to various degrees of uncertainty, with which Hume's considerations are mainly concerned. He first divides relations into two categories: those which depend upon knowledge derived from the senses, which are identity, spatio-temporal relations and causation, and the relations of logic and number. The last of those depending on the senses, causation, in Hume's view goes beyond immediate impressions of the senses and it is to causation that he directs his most searching examination. Events are individual and do not logically entail any other event. "'Tis only *causation* which produces such a connexion as to give us assurance from the existence or action of one object that 'twas followed or preceded by any other existence or action."

"It is evident that all reasonings concerning *matter of fact* are founded upon the relation of cause and effect and that we can never infer the existence of one object from another, unless they are connected together, either mediately or immediately. In order, therefore, to understand these reasonings, we must be perfectly acquainted with the idea of a cause."

The relation of cause and effect had always been assimilated to that between premises and conclusions in a logical argument. Hume now points out that causal relations can only be discovered as the result of experience. They cannot be found by examining the objects or events themselves. "There is no object which implies the existence of any other if we consider these objects in themselves and never look beyond the ideas which we form of them." The experience, moreover, on which the idea of causality rests is not simply that of the two objects concerned—the cause and effect— since nothing is discernible in the first which enables us to infer the second. The experience must be of the relation of the two events to each other. Thus Hume maintains that when we say that A causes B we merely imply that A is always conjoined to B. "We have no other notion of cause and effect, but that of certain objects which have been *always conjoined* together.... We cannot penetrate into the reason of the conjunction."

Hume's scepticism rests, therefore, on his rejection of induction. The principle of induction is that if a number of instances of one event being followed by another have been observed, then it becomes increasingly likely as the number of such observations increases that, on the next occasion of the first event occurring, the second will be found to follow. Unless this principle is valid, all scientific laws based upon generalisation from particular instances are without foundation. Unless the principle is valid it would be impossible to learn from experience. Clearly the principle cannot be established on the grounds that it has been found to work in the past, since it is precisely the conformability of the future to the past that is in question. The lack of success of attempts to refute the arguments of Hume would appear to indicate that a principle, such as the uniformity of nature, which lies outside the field of observation, is required to justify argument by induction.

Having arrived at these shattering conclusions, Hume confesses that he has no option, in the practical affairs of life, but to assume that induction, or the principle of causation, is valid, in spite of what he says. "It is impossible upon any system to defend either our understanding or our senses; and we but expose them further when we endeavour to justify them in that manner. As the sceptical doubt arises naturally from a profound and intense reflection on these subjects, it always increases the further we carry our reflections, whether in opposition or conformity to it. Carelessness and inattention alone can afford us any remedy. For this reason I rely entirely upon them; and take it for granted, whatever may be the reader's opinion at this present moment, that an hour hence he will be persuaded there is both an external and internal world."

Carelessness and inattention are a curious recommendation with which to commend the views to establish which an entire volume has just been written. Has Hume succeeded to quite the extent he imagined he had in destroying the value of reasoning concerning matters of fact? He has undoubtedly exposed its uncertain foundation but he has not provided any other basis for action in its place. As we have already seen, the only possible course of action open to us in such circumstances is to assume that our reasoning may be right and base our conduct upon it. If we adopt the contrary view that reasoning can give us no clue to the future, we would, like Buridan's ass, for ever remain rooted in our footsteps and unable to do anything at all. What action we take as a result of reasoning may well be wrong but it is the only line that we can take. This is rather different in principle from Hume's advocacy of carelessness and inattention and seems likely to give rather better results. We *may* at least avoid being run over by a bus in the street, which carelessness and inattention would hardly render possible. If the future happens to turn out to be conformable to the past, if only in a limited way, we shall naturally be better off through the adoption of the principle that it is; and if it turns out not to be so we shall be none the worse for having made the assumption.

Chapter XIV

THE APPEAL TO ORDINARY LANGUAGE, COMMON SENSE AND SENSE DATA

Berkeley's challenge to the evidence of a world external to our minds was a source of much perplexity and incredulity. Today, while few would wish to accept his solution of the problem, many, though by no means all, would agree that the problem was a real one. Indeed much of the philosophy of modern times is still connected with this question more or less directly. The objections of Berkeley and Hume to the view of common sense seemed, obviously, to possess force and no one was at all clear how they might be refuted. Yet it was equally clear that it is impossible to live one's ordinary life without the notion that we exist in a world of things, animate and inanimate, and that our lives have to be conditioned by the environment in which we find ourselves, including in that term the minds of those with whom we come into contact. How is the situation to be met?

Dr Johnson met it "with alacrity" by saying of Berkeley's thesis, "I refute it thus!" and, as Boswell records, "striking his foot with mighty force against a large stone, till he rebounded from it." Of a similar problem Dr Johnson said on another occasion, "Sir, we know that the will is free and there's an end on't." If philosophy disagrees with common sense, so much the worse for philosophy.

This attitude, or something remarkably like it, has been revived in more or less recent philosophical discussions. The movement, in its modern form, was initiated, or at least triggered off, by G. E. Moore. As early as 1903, while still holding his prize Fellowship at Trinity College, Cambridge, Moore had written a paper for *Mind* entitled *The Refutation of Idealism* in which he challenged the doctrine *"Esse* is *Percipi"* of Berkeley. Throughout his career at Cambridge, first as a Fellow of Trinity and then, after a break of seven years, as lecturer and later professor, Moore maintained his support of realism. In 1925 he contributed a paper to *Contemporary British Philosophy* entitled "A defence of Common Sense", and fourteen years later, in 1939, this was followed up with a famous lecture to

10   133

the British Academy (*Proc. of the British Academy, Vol. XXV* (1939)) under the title of "Proof of an External World". His "proof" follows almost exactly the same lines as did Dr Johnson, although the arguments had crystallised somewhat in the interval. "If I say of anything I am perceiving 'That is a soap bubble', I can, it seems to me, certainly imply that there would be no contradiction in asserting that it existed before I perceived it, and will continue to exist, even if I cease to perceive it. This seems to me part of what is meant by saying that it is a real soap bubble." He goes on a little later to give his "proof" of the external world. "I can prove now for instance" he says "that two human hands exist. How? By holding up my two hands, and saying, as I make a certain gesture with my right hand 'Here is one hand', and adding, as I make a certain gesture with the left 'And here is another'."

Such a statement is clearly an assertion, not a proof. It would amount to a proof only if his statement "Here is one hand and here is another" is accepted as true, and that would, of course, beg the very question at issue. Moore, in fact, admits in his lecture that if what is meant by proof is a deduction based upon general statements in the normal manner, then he has not given one and he adds that he does not believe that one can be given. What he appears to be saying is this. No statement can be made, of the truth of which we can be more sure than we are of the truth of those made about the external world. The existence of the external world is known to us and must be among the premises from which any discussion must start. The external world embodies the very meaning we attach to the word exist. To question it is absurd. If philosophical arguments appear to question it, there must be something wrong with the philosophical arguments. It is time philosophers ceased to doubt or pretend to doubt the existence of an external world. It is really too ridiculous. "How absurd it would be to suggest that I did not know it (the existence of his hands) but only believed it, and that perhaps it was not the case. You might as well suggest that I do not know that I am standing up and talking—and that perhaps after all I'm not, and that it is not quite certain that I am!"

Moore claims to *know* of the existence of the external world and that there is nothing of which we can be more sure, and his position is by no means implausible. What is given by him is not a proof so much as a discussion of the grounds upon which all proofs must be based. This can be advocated but it cannot very well be argued on the basis of accepted principles. The method of advocacy he employs in favour of adopting the basis he desires consists in ridiculing the opposite view. His task was one of persuasion and this he attempted to accomplish by the most effective method he could find at his disposal. In fact, many were converted to his point of view and it would not be untrue to say that he founded a new school of philosophy upon his principles. Other principles were soon added to them. It is of the nature of axioms, however, that it is impossible to compel another person to accept them by advancing conclusive arguments in their favour. It is true that unless agreement can be reached that certain premisses can be accepted, at least for purposes of discussion, no rational discourse of any kind can be carried on. Nevertheless, it must always remain open for anyone who does not like the set of axioms commonly employed to reject them and to introduce a new set of his own. This was precisely what Moore did in his *Proof of an External World*. His argument can, therefore, never lead to finality. In spite of the conclusions about the meaninglessness of metaphysical questions which were drawn from these premisses, they could only be maintained on the basis of the new axioms. To anyone adopting a different set of axioms it could appear, as indeed it did to some, that the conclusions arrived at by this school of philosophy were just as nonsensical.

Moore, as we have seen, maintained that he had knowledge of the external world though he might not be able to show how he knew what he knew. His method of argument was based upon two principles, one of which was the correctness of common sense and the other was analysis. By analysis Moore did not mean linguistic analysis by which the meaning of one statement is identified with the meaning of another. This, he pointed out, could be done without discussing the meaning of either. Analysis, according to him, must be of the concepts or ideas conveyed by the statement.*

How far his acceptance of common sense went may now seem rather doubtful, though at the time he gave the impression that it was the ultimate arbiter. In clarifying his meaning at a later date he seems to have reduced the scope of his canon of common sense very considerably. Many had taken him at face value to mean that philosophy cannot question the statements of common sense the truth of which was already known. However, in 1942 he wrote: "I have sometimes distinguished between two propositions each of which has been made by some philosophers, namely, (1) the proposition 'There are no material things' and (2) the proposition 'Nobody knows for certain that there are any material things.' And in ... my British Academy lecture called *Proof of an External World* ... I implied that with regard to the first of these propositions that it could be proved false ... by holding up one of my hands ... But with regard to the second of these two propositions, which has, I think, been far more commonly asserted than the first, I do not think I

* *Philosophy of G. E. Moore*, p. 662.

have ever implied that *it* could be *proved* to be false in any such simple way....

"Some philosophers have sometimes so used the expression 'material thing' that if 'phenomenalism' (in one of its senses) is true, i.e., for example, if the sun, and the moon and the earth and human bodies etc. etc. are all merely 'logical fictions' or 'logical constructions out of sense data' or 'permanent possibilities of sensation' then these objects are not 'material things'; and have used 'there are no material things' merely to mean that phenomenalism, in this sense, *is* true. So used, the assertion 'there are no material things' is merely an assertion that a certain kind of analysis of such a proposition as 'This is a human hand' is true; and it is obvious that from the truth of the assertion 'This is a human hand' it cannot follow that this analysis is false. With this meaning of 'There are no material things' then it is really impossible to prove that the statement is false in the way I gave."

With this admission Moore draws what appeared to be the most dangerous of the teeth of his demonstration. Few would wish to maintain that there is no sense in which it would be true to say that an external world exists. If it can be agreed that the term "exists" can embrace "logical constructions out of sense data" there are not many who would feel uneasy. As Wittgenstein remarked "Those philosophers who have denied the existence of matter have not wished to deny that under my trousers I wear pants." Moore, however, disagrees with this view and thinks that some have indeed maintained just that, so that his proof is still necessary.

A movement once started tends to gather momentum. Moore's championship of the common sense view of the external world led to a rise in the esteem in which common sense in general was held in philosophical circles. Whenever philosophy differed from common sense it was the latter which was to be preferred. For example, it came to be maintained that philosophical paradoxes arose through the misuse of ordinary language. Words were given meanings they did not ordinarily possess and the results were the "worries" which perplexed the philosophers. This extension of the realm of common sense to include common linguistic usage was something which grew naturally out of the original position of Moore. Those who accepted it thought that the correct way to deal with philosophical worries was to analyse the meaning of the words and expressions used to state them. The philosophical problems themselves could not be *solved* in this way; they rather dissolved when their true nature was appreciated and they came to be seen to be not problems at all. The terms in which they had been propounded turn out to be meaningless in the way in which they had been employed.

Philosophical worries, it was thought, could be removed by a linguistic analysis of a peculiarly elementary kind.

One of the most ardent champions of the supremacy of common language was Norman Malcolm. He professed to be doing nothing more than using Moore's own arguments. "... there are" he said (*The Philosophy of G. E. Moore*, p. 356) "two ways in which a person may be wrong when he makes an empirical statement. First, he may be making a mistake as to what the empirical facts are. Second, he may know all right what the empirical facts are, but may use the wrong language to describe those facts. We might call the first 'being wrong about the facts' and the second 'using incorrect language' or 'using improper language' or 'using wrong language.'

"It is true that at one time everyone said that the earth was flat, and what everyone said was wrong.... The way in which their statement was wrong was that they were making a mistake about the facts, not that they were using incorrect language; they were using perfectly correct language to describe what they thought to be the case. In the sense in which they said what was wrong it is perfectly possible for *everyone* to say what is wrong.

"Now suppose a case where two people agree as to what the empirical facts are, and yet disagree in their statements. For example, two people are looking at an animal; they have a clear close up view of it. Their descriptions of the animal are in perfect agreement. Yet one of them says it is a fox, and the other says it is a wolf. Their disagreement could be called linguistic.

"Now suppose that there were a case like the one preceding with this exception: that the one who says it is a wolf not only agrees with the other man as to what the characteristics of the animal are, but furthermore *agrees that that sort of animal is ordinarily called a fox*. If he were to continue to insist that it is a wolf, we can see how absurd would be his position. He would be saying that although the other man was using an expression to describe a certain situation which was the expression ordinarily employed to describe that sort of situation, nevertheless the other man was using incorrect language. What makes his statement absurd is that ordinary language *is* correct language.

The authors of the philosophical paradoxes commit this very absurdity, although in a subtle and disguised way.

"... But the philosopher who says that the ordinary person is mistaken when he says that he sees the cat in the tree, does not mean that he sees a squirrel rather than a cat; does not mean that it is a mirage; does not mean that it is an hallucination. He will agree that the facts of the situation are what we should ordinarily describe by the expression 'seeing a cat in a tree'. Nevertheless, he says that the man does not really see a cat; he sees only sense data of a cat. Now if it gives the philosopher pleasure to substitute the expression 'I see some sense-data of my wife', for the expression 'I see my wife', etc., then he is at liberty thus to express himself, providing he warns people beforehand so that they will understand him. But when he says the man does not *really* see a cat, he commits a great absurdity; for he implies that a person can use an expression to describe a certain state of affairs which is the expression ordinarily used to describe just such a state of affairs, and yet be using incorrect language.

"... In the case of all expressions the meanings of which must be *shown* and cannot be explained, ... it follows from the fact that they are ordinary expressions in the language that there have been *many* situations of the kind which they describe; otherwise so many people could not have learned the correct use of those expressions. Whenever a philosophical paradox asserts, therefore, with regard to such an expression, that always when that expression is used the use of it produces a false statement, then to prove that the expression is an *ordinary* expression is completely to refute the paradox."

This refutes the paradox, however, only in the case of those philosophers who have been sufficiently incautious as to deny there is *any* sense in which the expression "I see a cat in a tree" can be true,—only, that is, in the case of those who wish to deny the existence of pants under the trousers. It does not remove the problem of the analysis of the expression, by determining in what sense it may be true and in what sense it is false.

The doctrine of the correctness of ordinary language, however, has been frequently taken at its face value. There can be little doubt that Malcolm, for example, felt that he was removing perplexing difficulties which philosophers had raised. When an ordinary man has a certain experience he exclaims "I see a cat in a tree" and Malcolm adds, "There's an end on't." The ordinary man could not be wrong because having the experience is just what the expression means. That is undoubtedly true. However, it leaves unanswered the question what is the nature of the experience. The result of the appeal to ordinary language is certainly true but from a philosophical point of view its conclusion is trivial.

That such a result would come from an appeal to ordinary language might, perhaps, have been expected. Ordinary language evolved at a time when the nature of perception was not understood, before in fact anyone had ever thought of examining it, and before any of its problems had been appreciated. It can hardly then be expected that common language will be found to contain answers to questions about the nature of perception. The dissolution of philosophical difficulties only arises through the fact that in confining ourselves to ordinary language we restrict ourselves to a vocabulary in which they cannot be expressed. No one would suggest that philosophy is immune from muddles or that some of these could not be due to the misuse of language. Indeed, it is probable that a linguistic therapy has its uses. On the other hand a philosopher who wishes to examine ordinary concepts, such as those involved in seeing a cat in a tree, is bound to disagree with an axiom about the ultimate correctness of ordinary language which does not possess the vocabulary in which his problem can be expressed.

The appeal to ordinary language acts as a philosophical narcotic. The degree of ordinariness which is required in the language has varied to some extent according to the practitioner conducting the therapeutic analysis. At one extreme is the suggestion that it must be capable of being understood by Bertie Wooster. "We Woosters have a fine sense of what is fitting."* It would appear difficult to defend a policy of adopting as arbiter of ordinary usage, and thus of the concepts of philosophy, the language of a character such as Bertie Wooster. Those who appeal to ordinary language tend to say that they mean standard English—a thing most difficult to define, if, indeed, it can be said to exist at all—or the language of ordinary people—of the man on the top of the Clapham omnibus, to borrow a phrase employed in another sphere. Why should it be standard English rather than standard French or Welsh? Since fewer philosophical ideas are likely to be contained in a language the more primitive it is, it would appear that the primitive languages should be the most effective in removing philosophical "worries". The basis for their removal consists in their being absent from the language in which the therapy is being conducted. Those who are not mathematically inclined rarely employ the language of mathematics. By this means they succeed in preventing mathematics from worrying them though they do not often accompany their avoiding action with the suggestion that mathematicians are talking nonsense!

An example of a piece of linguistic analysis was given by Professor Ryle in his Tarner Lectures in 1953. He chose to consider the doctrine of fatalism, the doctrine that is "that what is, had to be". He chose it for the very sound reason that it had not been held vehemently by any school of philosophy so that it was easier to consider it dispassionately than a more controversial subject. The doctrine of fatalism is not quite the same as the theological doctrine of predestation though it is an ingredient in it. In the doctrine of predestation it is assumed that the future is known to some being beforehand. The doctrine of fatalism does not require that anyone

* Stephen Toulmin, *Proc. Arist. Soc.* 1949–50.

need actually know what is to take place. The future may be inescapable even if nobody knows what it is to be. On Sunday Professor Ryle coughed and went to bed at a certain hour. It was already true on the previous Saturday that at that hour on the Sunday evening Professor Ryle would cough and go to bed. If it was true beforehand then it would be impossible for him not to do it. The argument is quite general. It was true a thousand years ago that on that particular Sunday evening Professor Ryle would cough and go to bed. It can be applied to all events.

Faced with one who accepted this doctrine, and we all from time to time have feelings of the same kind—during a war there is or there is not a bullet with our name on it in the enemy's arsenals—we might try to rid him of his obsession by examining its meaning in ordinary language.

First we examine the statement "It was true". It could mean that if someone had made the prediction it would have turned out to be true. Can a "might have been" prediction be true? There is also a slur in the word false and honour in the word true. We therefore, substitute the words correct and incorrect for the words true and false. We reformulate the doctrine in terms of an antecedent guess turning out to be correct. It sounds far less alarming.

Next we turn to the question of guessing. Some make correct guesses about the result of a horse race, but the correctness of their guess does not make the horse win the race. To believe this would be "quite false". (The pejorative false creeps in in spite of our care.) Can the guess be correct until the race is run?

Correct and incorrect are adjectives which make one think of a property resident in a substance, like sweetness in sugar. The qualities we wish to describe should be assimilated rather to "obituary" adjectives like deceased, lamented and extinct.

What sort of necessity is the fatalistic necessity for an event to happen? After an event has happened it will always remain true that it has happened. This posterior truth does not alarm us whereas the anterior truth does. The anterior truth suggests a cause. Events cannot be the effects of their successors. We must, therefore, examine words like necessitating, making, obliging, requiring, involving and their relation to causing. As a result we arrive at "the very dull truth" that for everything that happens there is a certain guess which will turn out to be correct. It tells us nothing about how the event was caused. A forecaster cannot get the future events themselves for the heroes of history. Novelists write in the past tense.

With a discussion about events which might have been, this completes the analysis. It certainly is ample to persuade us, who, as it happens, need no elaborate process of convincing, of the absurdity of the fatalistic position, but we had no very firm conviction of its validity in the first place. It is one of the difficulties in explaining away a worry which few have actually experienced to any extent, that the arguments lack opposition. Can we place ourselves in the position of one who really accepted the doctrine to start with? Would the arguments of Professor Ryle convince him? The very brief summary of these arguments given here is, no doubt, most inadequate and should be taken as nothing more than an indication of the nature of the complete exposition, the setting out of which occupies forty-two paragraphs in the original account of the lecture.

The argument consists in a statement of the opposite thesis in as many different and as plausible ways as possible in the hope that some of them may be acceptable. There is no compulsion. All the analyst hopes for is that the light may dawn. It is not easy for us to imagine the defences which a supporter of the doctrine of fatalism would employ to counter the arguments Professor Ryle puts forward, but it is difficult to believe that he would be converted by the Professor's case. When, for example, he was confronted with the difference between anterior and posterior truths, would he not say that it was this difference that he finds puzzling? Alternatively he might put the case round the other way and turn the tables on the analyst by pointing out that the argument cuts both ways. We do not doubt posterior truths so why should we doubt the anterior? Or when he is faced with the correct guess of the result of the horse race would he not readily admit that the guessing correctly did not cause the horse to win, since he would have felt the same had no one made the guess at all? Moreover it is quite likely that he would not agree to the classification of the statement "It was true, it had to be" along with guessing at all. It is not somebody making a guess that worries him. The future will be what it will be—and this can hardly be doubted—and this it is which is the essence of his difficulty.

Linguistic philosophers make considerable use of what is known as the paradigm case. This is the case which is supposed to show the correct use of a word or phrase, or to show up a conflict in their use. For example, the employment of "object words" in standard English is taken as the proof of the existence of material things. The paradigm case shows how such words may be employed in the language. The employment of words describing the feelings of others, similarly proves that we cannot question our ability to know what others feel. But we need not elaborate the details of the arguments employed. They are only convincing within the limits of the system and thus only to those who accept the premises with which the argument starts. It has to be assumed that all problems are capable of being expressed in ordinary language.

In all such cases, when it is argued that some philosophical conclusion is sense or nonsense, we are not arguing within a system the basis of which is acceptable to both sides. There are no agreed premisses from which a start may be made. Obviously if we employ the correctness of common language among those premisses we can never arrive at any conclusion which is at variance with it, however long we argue—so long, that is, as we do it correctly. If we accept with Moore the principle of the inviolability of common sense, similarly no question at variance with common sense can arise as a meaningful problem. At the same time we can never be sure of convincing one who does not limit himself to these premisses. The mark of those philosophers who raised these philosophical questions which the linguistic analysts sought to dissolve, was that they did not limit themselves to common sense or common language. In fact they pointed out that common sense and common language were formulated long before such questions had arisen, so that it would have been a physical impossibility for them to have been incorporated into either. Within their limits, no new question can ever arise meaningfully. Further, the philosophical views at the time were of the crudest and anyone being guided by them in philosophical matters will be more than likely to be misled.

G. E. Moore went up to Trinity College in 1892. He was elected Fellow in 1898. Two years his senior in the same College was Bertrand Russell, and the two were in intimate contact for many years. Russell, who also became a Fellow of the College, like Moore, felt that it was absurd to question or to pretend to question the existence of a world external to our minds. For Moore it was common sense that provided knowledge of the external world. Russell took a rather different line. For him it was science that provided the most reliable knowledge that we could obtain. He was well aware of the uncertain nature of scientific knowledge and also that scientific theories possessed different degrees of credibility and that when first put forward they might be doubtful in the extreme.

"Every physical theory" he said, "which survives goes through three stages. In the first stage, it is a matter of controversy among specialists; in the second stage the specialists are agreed that it is the theory which best fits the available evidence, though it may well hereafter be found incompatible with new evidence; in the third stage it is thought very unlikely that any new evidence will do more than somewhat modify it.

"When I say that I shall assume physics to be true, I mean that I shall accept those parts of physics which have reached the third stage, not as certain, but as more probable than any philosophical speculation, and, therefore, proper to be accepted by philosophers as a premiss in their arguments." (*Human Knowledge*, p. 214.)

The positions taken up by both Moore and Russell possess a certain similarity. Both accept that it is possible to obtain knowledge of the external world, Moore via the medium of common sense, Russell via science. Moore confesses that he is unable to decide what the correct analysis of his assumption of the validity of common sense should be. Russell examines his belief in the validity of science.

He does not, however, accept scientific knowledge as the kind of knowledge of which we are the most certain. This distinction belongs to the immediate data of the senses. Since, in this book, we desire to examine the nature of scientific theories, Russell's approach is of particular interest to us. "...It is clear that the relation of a percept to the physical object which is supposed to be perceived is vague, approximate and somewhat indefinite. There is no precise sense in which we can be said to perceive physical objects." (*Human Knowledge* p. 223.) Besides the immediate data which are provided by the senses, which are insufficient of themselves to construct the physical world, Russell is prepared to utilise, in addition, memory of similar data from the past. This view of the fundamental nature of sense data is a form of empiricism and the school which accepts it has been typical of British philosophy.

Sense data, present to the mind or in the memory, however, do not even then suffice of themselves to build the world of science. In addition some principle of probable inference is required. Such a principle is necessary if a transition is to be effected from the data given immediately by the senses or indirectly via the memory, to an external world. It is also required if a transition from the particular facts inferred from the sense data to the general laws of science is to be possible.

Finally, to be able to base his philosophical reasoning upon the premisses of the picture of things presented by physics, Russell has to accept two further principles which are incorporated into physical theories in the course of their construction. One of these is the principle derived from Locke already mentioned, namely that it is only necessary to take into account the position and motion of material particles in space. All secondary qualities are to be interpreted in terms of these. (At one time the study of secondary, qualitative differences concerned another branch of science—for example chemistry—but modern theory of the atom has incorporated chemistry within physics.) The second principle incorporated into physics, was that of the independent action of causes—that the motion of a particle in a short time, for example, under the influence of a number of forces, is the same as though the forces acted separately, one after the other for the same short time. These assumptions seem much more detailed than those that are commonly incorporated into a philosophy, but since Russell is convinced that scientific knowledge is the best at present attainable, he is obliged to record these among his premisses.

Thus Russell would regard logical and mathematical statements, together with sense-data and memory, as providing knowledge in the strict sense of that word. He would regard the world of science (physics) as a belief founded upon the second group and using the first, and he would regard the world of common sense as a misinterpretation of them, though acceptable as a first approximation.

Such a theory of knowledge undoubtedly possesses a considerable appeal to those who have been brought up on science or who are engaged in practising it. Little change of attitude is called for on their part. It is the philosophy which most of them have adopted and acted upon almost unconsciously. It does not claim that science provides certain knowledge and it does not neglect entirely philosophical objections. These are recognised for what they are and their justification for the most part admitted. They are pointers to the assumptions which have to be made if science is to provide knowledge.

Science is certainly prepared to question the dicta of common language and of common sense. In so far as it does this it will represent a higher level of sophistication than can be furnished by appeal to the common language of the linguistic analysts or to the common sense of Moore. The premisses of any philosophy are composed of those statements which it is not proposed to question. The limitations of a philosophy which starts from the premisses of scientific dicta will largely coincide with the limits of science itself. It can hardly be accepted, however, if any attempt is to be made to criticise the findings of science.

We might now attempt to summarise the principal conclusions to be drawn from this chapter. They are that a philosophy based upon the correctness of the usages of common language will be adequate to deal with the problems which arise through the misuse of common language. Since common language arose out of the doings of common people in their day to day living, it is unlikely to be able to deal with problems which go deeper than this. In particular it will be beyond its powers to deal satisfactorily with mistakes inherent in common language itself. Similar remarks apply to the common sense philosophy of G. E. Moore. Errors of common sense will be excluded from consideration. It seems reasonable to suppose that common sense is prior to common language so that all the errors of common sense will be built into common language but not necessarily vice-versa. It is to be expected that common sense will be somewhat more versatile than the philosophy based upon ordinary language. Common sense objections to ordinary usage will be possible. On the other hand, Russell's scientific philosophy will be much more versatile than either of the others. Based upon a much deeper level of sophistication, a correspondingly greater range of problems may be expected to be thrown up by it. Its limits will be the "established" scientific theories, which it accepts as providing knowledge.

Each of these systems has its uses, and would be appropriate according to the level of discourse adopted. There is a sense in which the world of common sense is valid. If we do not wish to carry our investigations further than is appropriate to this level, all will be well. There is another sense in which the world described by science is valid, and at a different level of discourse, it provides the appropriate vocabulary for the discussion. None of them, however, can be regarded as absolute. In adopting any one of them we must agree beforehand to limit ourselves to questions which can be raised meaningfully within its boundaries.

Chapter XV

LOGICAL CONSTRUCTIONS AND
INFERRED ENTITIES

According to the views of Bertrand Russell the only things of which we are directly aware are sense-data. "What can we learn by observation and experiment? Nothing so far as physics is concerned, except immediate data of sense: certain patches of colour, sounds, tastes, smells etc. with certain spatio-temporal relations." But "molecules have no colour, atoms make no noise, electrons have no taste and corpuscles do not even smell." (*Mysticism and Logic*, p. 138. Penguin edition.) How then can observation and experiment verify the existence of such entities? Russell suggests two possible ways out of this difficulty. In the first place we might make use of some *a priori* principle not given in sensation, by assuming, for example, that our sense data have causes. In so far as this solution is adopted physics ceases to be empirical or based upon experiment and observation alone. This method should, therefore, be avoided as far as possible.

Alternatively we might try defining the objects of physics in terms of sense-data. The usual way of presenting the relation between sense-data and physical objects is to make it appear that sense-data are caused by physical objects. If physics is to remain verifiable then this relation must be put the other way round. The only things which are directly verifiable are the sense-data; physical objects must be defined in terms of them. When we refer to a physical object we must take it that the reference is to a certain concatenation of actual or possible sense-data.

Possible sense-data, that is to say sense-data which are not actually being observed but which could be observed if an observer were there to experience them, Russell calls sensibilia. He finds it necessary to include them together with sense-data from the past derived from the memory and actual sense-data being experienced at the present time, in order to construct the world with which physics deals. Armed with these he is able to show how the space-time of physics, physical objects and matter can be derived as logical constructions.

"Since the 'thing' cannot" he says "without indefensible partiality, be identified with any of its appearances, it came to be thought

146

of as something distinct from all of them and underlying them. But by the principle of Occam's razor, if the class of appearances will fulfil the purposes for the sake of which the thing was invented by the prehistoric metaphysicians to whom common sense is due, economy demands that we should identify the thing with the class of its appearances. It is not necessary to *deny* a substance or substratum underlying these appearances; it is merely expedient to abstain from asserting this unnecessary entity. ... The supreme maxim in scientific philosophising is this: *Whenever possible, logical constructions are to be substituted for inferred entities."* (*Mysticism and Logic* p. 148.)

"What is proved" (by the empirical success of physics) "is that its hypotheses, though unverifiable where they go beyond sense-data, are at no point in contradiction with sense-data, but, on the contrary, are ideally such as to render all sense-data calculable when a sufficient collection of 'sensibilia' is given. Now physics has found it possible to collect sense-data into series, each series being regarded as belonging to one 'thing', and behaving with regard to the laws of physics, in a way in which series not belonging to the one thing would, in general, not behave. ... *Physical things are those series of appearances whose matter obeys the laws of physics.* That such series exist is an empirical fact, which constitutes the verifiability of physics."

Let us, without more ado, assume that the objects of physics and their properties can be defined in this way, and, as an exercise, attempt to substitute in a physical theory which was developed on the basis of inferred entities, logical constructions according to the maxim of Bertrand Russell. To do this it will suffice if, for the inferred entities, we are able to substitute logical constructions framed in terms of those physical things which Bertrand Russell has, in turn, constructed from sensibilia. In other words, we substitute for the inferred entities, constructions of things which are directly observable in the usual sense of that term as employed in physics. The example we will take will be the atomic and molecular theory of chemistry as it was developed in the nineteenth century.

In this period the atomic theory of chemistry depended upon chemical evidence and it owed comparatively little to the atomic theory of physics—in the narrower sense of the term physics. Indeed, at that time, the debt was in the opposite direction. In the physical sciences attempts are often made to derive laws from propositions which are not simple generalisations of the direct results of experience but which are stated in terms of entities, such as atoms and molecules, which cannot be directly perceived. To this class belongs Newton's corpuscular theory of light, Huyghens' wave theory and the atomic theory of Dalton which we are now to consider. Properties have to be assigned to these entities which transcend the senses, to enable those properties possessed by matter in bulk, which are directly observable, to be accounted for. In the case of the atomic theory, for example, Dalton postulated that his atoms possessed the property of combining only in fixed ratios. There is, of course, not the slightest reason *a priori* why this should be so. Dalton was free to endow his atoms with any properties he pleased. He attributed this property of combining only in fixed ratios to his atoms, in order that he would be in a position to explain, thereby, the constancy of composition of chemical compounds already observed. What he did, in fact, was simply to transfer the property of matter in bulk directly to the atoms of which he supposed it to be composed. Similarly he transferred directly the property of matter in bulk described by the law of simple multiple proportions to his atoms, by postulating that they had the property of combining together only in simple ratios. Again this is an *ad hoc* hypothesis with no *a priori* reasons to support it. Such a procedure was adopted in the case of all the simple chemical laws which were at the disposal of chemists at the time. Up to the time of Cannizzaro, whose *Sketch* appeared in 1858, therefore, the atomic theory clearly consisted of a logical construction of the simplest and most direct kind, from the observed properties of matter in bulk, which, in their turn, can be interpreted in terms of sensibilia, on the lines indicated by Russell. What advance did this interpretation achieve over the group of chemical laws which it "explained"? Very little. A fresh hypothesis concerning the properties of the atom was required to interpret each observed law. Matter was indestructible because it was made of indestructible atoms. Each property of matter in bulk was mirrored by a similar property possessed by the atoms. The laws were as simple as the theory and the theory was as complicated as the laws. The atom was constructed by the simple process of transferring to it the properties of matter in bulk, just as they stood.

Cannizzaro gave a new look to chemical theory. The basis which he took for his work of clarification was "the touchstone of Avogadro". What he showed in his *Sketch* was that by taking the hypothesis of Avogadro as true, the whole of chemical theory, which until that time had been plagued by uncertainty, fell neatly into place. However, it is quite possible to develop the theory of chemistry to the stage at which Cannizzaro left it, without invoking the hypothesis of Avogadro at all. Instead of basing the theory of chemistry on this hypothesis which can never be verified directly, the hypothesis can be derived, or at least rendered more plausible, by a study of chemical theory. Further the whole structure is capable of being developed without the aid of an atomic theory at all. In order to see how this can come about it will be necessary to see how the Daltonian atoms and molecules can be interpreted as simple direct constructs out of the properties of matter in bulk.

The basis of the new advance made by Cannizzaro was, in fact, furnished by the reacting volumes of gases. The empirical laws relating the volumes in which gases react with one another and the volumes of the products of the reaction, if gaseous, had been given by Gay-Lussac. Gay-Lussac's law is that the volumes in which gases react bear a simple ratio to each other and to the volume of the gaseous product. It follows from this that if the same volume of a number of gaseous compounds, for example of hydrogen, are ana-lysed for that element, they will be found to contain multiples of a certain unit volume, or mass, of that element. To be precise, the largest volume of any hydrogen compound containing one gramme of that element was found to be 22·4 litres under standard conditions of temperature and pressure. Under those conditions that volume of any compound of hydrogen in the gaseous state contains one, two, three or an integral number of grammes of the element. In the same volume of any gaseous compound of oxygen were found 16, 32, 48—or integral multiples of 16 grammes of oxygen. There is, of course, no particular virtue in working with a volume of 22·4 litres. Any volume will serve; the only difference will be that the unit mass found for the elements will be different, though they will continue to bear the same ratios to one another.

It is usual to start the consideration of the theory by taking, as was originally intended, hydrogen to be the basis of measurement. Let us call the unit mass of hydrogen found in our chosen volume of a large number of hydrogen compounds, unity. The choice is quite arbitrary and today, of course, the basis has been shifted to that of oxygen taken as 16 for historical reasons. However, that is a refinement that does not affect the argument. The convenience of employing 22·4 litres for our chosen volume is that our unit of mass then becomes 1 gramme. Let us further call the unit mass of any element found in our chosen volume of a large number of its com-pounds in the gaseous state, its reacting mass. The reacting mass of hydrogen will thus be one. That of oxygen will be 16 and so on for all the elements which form gaseous compounds. The reacting mass of any element will obviously be identical with what was called its atomic weight on the atomic theory. In its derivation, however, the word atom has now not been mentioned. Chemists may protest that accurate atomic weights are actually determined gravimetrically and not by the analysis of gases. While this is true it does not affect the argument. Gravimetric analysis is employed solely because

11

it is more accurate than gaseous analysis. It involves no new conceptual insights. We can define reacting mass to be a multiple of the equivalent weight given approximately by the reacting volumes of gases, if we wish, and still retain a "construction out of sense-data".

Let us consider the combination of two gaseous elements, for example, that of hydrogen and oxygen to form water. If 22·4 litres of water in the gaseous state are analysed it will be found that they contain 2 grammes of hydrogen and 16 grammes of oxygen, that is, 2 reacting masses of hydrogen and one reacting mass of oxygen. The formula for water would, therefore, be written H_2O. And it is obvious that the formulae of all other gaseous compounds could be arrived at in a similar manner. If we take 22·4 litres of hydrogen itself we find it contains two grammes of the element. The formula for hydrogen would therefore be H_2. Similarly that for oxygen, as a result of the same measurement for that element, would be found to be O_2.

Further, armed with a number of reacting masses of the elements derived in this manner, empirical rules, like that of Dulong and Petit, expressed in terms of the product of the reacting mass and the specific heat (in place of atomic weight and specific heat) or the law of isomorphous crystals, etc. would become available for elements which did not form any gaseous compounds or which formed too few for the argument to be satisfactory.

The chemical formulae of all compounds would thereby clearly become available equally on this system as on the atomic theory. The term atom need never be mentioned nor need the concept of an atom be made use of. The atoms would have been replaced by constructions formed from purely macroscopic observations, which, in turn, are replaceable in terms of directly experienced sense-data.

The so-called anomalous cases, attributed to gaseous polymerisation or dissociation, present no greater difficulties in terms of our constructs than in terms of atoms. When there is a gradual dissociation, as it is described in terms of the atomic theory, with rise in temperature, for example, as in the case of nitrogen peroxide, the simple whole number rule of Gay-Lussac breaks down. At low temperatures the formula of nitrogen peroxide approximates to N_2O_4 and at higher temperatures to NO_2. Evidently there are two compounds corresponding to the two formulae and the anomalous results are to be accounted for on the basis of there being a mixture of the two. Again we need no mention of the terms atom or molecule.

How far the process of the replacement of inferred entities by logical constructions out of quantities directly observed can be carried, and how simple the process is, we will not discuss further. We have taken it far enough for our purposes and clearly it need not end where we have left it. At higher levels the pieces in the game are the concepts formulated in the lower—formulae, groups commonly found reacting together as wholes, and the like. Valency would arise in connection with the relation of equivalent weights to reacting masses.

Let us, on the other hand, now discuss what has been achieved by this process of constructing concepts out of sense-data. There is first what might appear the somewhat academic achievement of demonstrating that chemistry is an empirical science not dependent upon particulars not verifiable by the senses. This amounts to an epistemological clarification of the basis of the subject. To carry it out thoroughly would be a task comparable to the demonstration of the logical basis of mathematics by such as Frege, Peano, Russell and Whitehead. Secondly the demonstration would show the logical structure of the theory of the subject and how each proposition in it depended upon the others. For example, it would show that the periodic table of the elements, which would now be made dependent upon reacting masses in place of atomic weights, would occupy a very basic position. It would survive any alteration which came to be made in the atomic theory. Indeed it would be capable of surviving the demise of the entire atomic theory itself.

One of the most important motives for the pursuit of science is the hope that it may elucidate the ultimate structure of matter. Great importance has become attached to the atomic theory in this connection. "...there is at least one problem in which all thinking men are interested. It is the problem of cosmology: *the problem of understanding the world—including ourselves, and our knowledge as part of the world.* All science is cosmology, I believe, and for me the interest of philosophy as well as of science lies solely in the contributions which they have made to it. For me at any rate, both philosophy and science would lose all their attraction if they were to give up that pursuit!" (Karl Popper: *Logic of Scientific Discovery*, p. 15). Many have indicated their belief that we, indeed, now *know* that matter is composed of atoms and that this can no longer seriously be doubted. In their view the atomic theory is true, in its main lines at least, if not in minute detail. Bertrand Russell, as we have seen, was prepared to use the interpretation of the external world provided by science as the premises in any philosophical discussion. He did not accept such knowledge as science provides as certain, and doubtless those who have expressed themselves with certainty about it would, if pressed, confess to a measure of philosophic doubt inherent in it. The degree of certainty attaching to scientific explanations couched in terms of inferred entities inaccessible directly to the senses, can only be assessed by considering the evidence which supports such views. How does the development of the explanations in terms of logical constructs affect the credibility of what is virtually the same explanation given in terms of the inferred entities?

At the turn of the century, when the theory of chemistry stood roughly in the position just described, there were those who rejected an atomic interpretation of the phenomena altogether. Among them, for example, was Ostwald, who favoured a theory based upon energetics. On the other hand there were others, and these were undoubtedly in the great majority, who regarded the phenomena of chemistry as furnishing very telling evidence in favour of an atomic explanation. Between these extremes there were, no doubt, a considerable number who looked upon the atomic theory as a convenient working hypothesis, and little more.

The synthesis of the theory of chemistry directly out of sense-data has the advantage of rendering it independent of inferred entities, the existence of which is bound to remain associated with a certain amount of doubt. Should evidence accrue from some other branch of science, for example, which led to the questioning of the reality of these entities, the theory of chemistry would remain unaffected. It would be capable of being constructed without reference to such entities at all. The theory of chemistry would then be directly verifiable by the senses and would be quite unaffected even if the names atoms and molecules could never be mentioned at all. Such an operational analysis as has just been sketched, provides the theory to which any explanation would have to conform. The formula for sulphuric acid will remain H_2SO_4 whatever explanation is put forward to account for it.

It would appear, at first sight, that if the theory of chemistry could be developed without mentioning the word atom at all, it could then hardly provide any evidence in favour of the existence of atoms. What the analysis does do is to free us from the language of the atomic theory and thus allow us to consider the question more dispassionately. To us who have been brought up to use that language the formulae of chemistry certainly appear to suggest an atomic explanation. Would they do so to those not so thoroughly steeped in the theory from the first? It is difficult to say. Fundamentally the situation remains unaltered. At no time were we ever entitled to say more than that matter behaves *as if* it was composed of atoms endowed with certain properties. Never were we entitled to say that it *is* so composed. After the theory has been constructed logically out of sense-data we are still entitled to go just as far as we were. The logical constructions arrived at are the same *as if* matter was composed of atoms endowed with the same properties as we had been accustomed to endow them with before.

Is the situation in which the atomic theory finds itself, therefore, similar to that of the aether in the theory of relativity? To some extent it is. There can be no objection to the employment of the idea of atoms if it helps us to think about the problems which remain unsolved, just as we can, if we wish, think in terms of an aether. On the other hand there is no necessity to do so if we would rather dispense with the idea altogether. In neither case can the existence of the inferred entity be demonstrated. It becomes to that extent superfluous and the principle which is associated with the name of William of Occam would recommend its elimination.

This is the situation as it existed at the turn of the century. Whether or not developments since that time have altered the situation at all radically we will leave for discussion elsewhere. It is not, however, the complete story. There is a point of fundamental importance in which a logical construct is defective. Logical constructions out of sense-data are admirable things with which to summarise knowledge which has already been obtained. They can clarify the position to which science has attained and in doing so remove a good deal of picturesque lumber. They introduce the utmost economy of ideas into the theoretical structure and they are empirically verifiable. On the other hand a logical construct contains no more than is contained in the empirical data which it summarises. It contains nothing extraneous, and it is in this that its virtue lies. At the same time it is in this that is to be found its most serious limitation. It contains nothing further on the basis of which "predictions" can be made. The observable facts out of which it is constructed imply no further facts if they are dissociated from any analogical element. The virtue of the inferred entity is that it goes beyond the facts and, therefore, suggests other applications.

This immediately raises a problem. Are the properties attributed to the inferred entity over and above what are contained in the logical constructions, justifiable? Clearly at the time before the "predictions" to which they lead have been tested, they are not, and it was for this reason that the word "prediction" was placed between inverted commas. One of the main uses to which an operational analysis can be put, therefore, is to sort out the justified from the unjustified among the properties attributed to the inferred entity. Future tests may lead to the latter being justified or alternatively to their having to be eliminated from the list of the properties of the entity. The analysis in terms of logical constructions out of sense-data shows us clearly what we can reasonably claim to know and what we cannot. What it does not do is to provide a route along which knowledge can be extended. On the other hand, the inferred entity shows the way to further knowledge, but in the end, like the scaffolding by which a building has been erected, it becomes unnecessary as soon as the building has been completed.

A further example may serve to make this clearer. According to the kinetic theory of gases, the pressure on the walls of a vessel containing a gas is attributable to the transfer of momentum to the walls as the molecules are reflected from them. A well-known simple calculation gives the pressure to be

$$p = \frac{1}{3} \rho \overline{V}^2$$

where ρ is the density of the gas and $\overline{V}$ the square root of the average value of the squares of the velocities of the molecules. On the assumption that $\overline{V}$ remains constant so long as the temperature remains constant, this gives,

$$\frac{p}{\rho} = \text{constant}$$

or Boyle's law. Now Boyle's law is directly observable and is of the simplest character. The kinetic theory of gases, on the other hand, involves many more concepts than are necessary to comprehend the law of Boyle by itself. On the other hand, the law suggests nothing other than itself. Against this the movement of the molecules of the gas to and fro suggests that the velocity with which a gas will stream through a small orifice will be proportional to V. That is to say, at constant pressure and temperature, the rate at which a gas emerges from the orifice will be inversely proportional to the square root of its density. This is Graham's law of gaseous diffusion which has been verified experimentally. The inferred entity, in the shape of the molecules moving to and fro with a certain velocity, therefore, leads beyond the law which initially gave rise to it and which would be all that would be available from the logical construct, before Graham's law had been discovered.

The inferred entity is thus capable of leading to further predictions which its counterpart, the logical construction out of sense-data, cannot. The "prediction" is, in fact, the direct result of the inclusion among the properties of the inferred entities, some which are unjustified by the existing evidence. The operational analysis can show what these additional properties are so that their consequences can be investigated. On this view, the "predictions" would appear to be the result of chance and their confirmation improbable. The alternative view would be that there exists some law of nature to the effect that if two things possess a certain number of properties in common, they are likely to possess other properties in common also. The validity of such a proposition is extremely doubtful. It is impossible to say whether predictions are frequently confirmed or not; failures are rarely recorded. The great *éclat* attaching to a successful prediction would appear to indicate that the process is not very common. It is unnecessary to assume that predictions are frequently confirmed. The mark of the scientist is that he is able to recognise those properties inherent in an inferred entity which have so far been without empirical basis. These are the properties which lie outside the alternative logical construct. They furnish him with the means of asking relevant questions and of refining the theory as a result of the tests to which these point. Perhaps "predictions" is a word which is too heavily and optimistically loaded to be appropriate in the context. Perhaps "possibilities to be investigated" would be better. When all is said and done, however, it is through the investigation of such possibilities that science progresses.

Chapter XVI

FALSIFICATION

An entirely different and original line of attack on the problems of the scientific method, and on that of induction in particular, was developed by Professor Karl Popper. In 1934 he wrote a book under the title of *Logik der Forschung*, an English translation of which, called the *Logic of Scientific Discovery*, was published in 1959. In this book he sought not so much to provide solutions to these problems which have troubled the philosophy of science, as to reformulate them in such a manner that they become amenable to the ordinary rules of logic, or were taken outside the field of logic altogether.

Logic deals with the validity of argument. It operates within a homogeneous system of sentences and is concerned with the entailment of one sentence by another. It thus puts on one side, as outside its terms of reference, two of the fundamental problems concerning scientific knowledge, namely the origin of the initial premises from which the argument starts, at one end, and the comparison of the conclusions with the data furnished by the senses, at the other. Each of these lies outside the province of the consideration of sentences and we shall have to return to them again before concluding the subject.

Popper regards science as a hypothetico-deductive system and his examination of the problem starts with the hypothesis or theory of the science as given. By this is not meant that he accepts them as true, far from it, but he is not concerned to discuss how they originated. He thus distinguishes carefully between the *psychology of knowledge* and the *logic of knowledge*. "The initial stage, the act of conceiving or inventing a theory" he says, "seems to me neither to call for logical analysis nor to be susceptible of it. The question how it happens that a new idea occurs to a man—whether it is a musical theme, a dramatic conflict or a scientific theory—may be of great interest to empirical psychology; but it is irrelevant to the logical analysis of scientific knowledge. This latter is not concerned with *questions of fact* (Kant's *quid facti?*) but only with questions of *justification or validity* (Kant's *quid juris?*). Its questions are of the following kind. Can a statement be justified? And, if so, how? Is it testable? Is it logically dependent on certain other statements?

Or does it perhaps contradict them? In order that a statement may be logically examined in this way it must already have been presented to us. Someone must have formulated it and submitted it to logical examination." (*Logic of Scientific Discovery*, p. 31.)

At one end of the chain of reasoning lie the hypotheses, at the other, according to Popper, occur "basic statements". These are statements which we decide to accept as describing what is the case. The acceptance may be for the time being only, but their acceptance is a question for decision which does not concern the logic of the argument. "...whether statements of logic are in question or statements of empirical science, I think the answer is the same: our *knowledge*, which may be described vaguely as a system of *dispositions*, and which may be of concern to psychology, may be in both cases linked with feelings of belief or conviction: in the one case, perhaps, with the feeling of being compelled to think in a certain way; in the other with that of 'perceptual assurance'. But all this interests only the psychologist. It does not even touch upon problems like those of the logical connections between scientific statements, which alone interest the epistemologists." (*L.S.D.*, p. 99.) "Nobody would dream of justifying the validity of a logical inference, or of defending it against doubts, by writing beside it in the margin the following protocol sentence. 'Protocol: In checking this chain of inferences today, I experienced an acute feeling of conviction'." (*L.S.D.*, p. 98.)

Scientific knowledge should be justifiable independently of anybody's whim and it should be testable and understandable by anyone. This implies "mutual rational control by critical discussion" (L.S.D., p. 44). Sooner or later, however, we have to stop. We must at some time or another be able to agree on what can be accepted for the time being. Deductions which can be made from scientific hypotheses or theories can then be testable against "basic sentences"—that is, sentences upon which agreement has, for the time being, been reached. Of course, it would be open to anybody to disagree with the acceptance of a basic sentence. In such a case its origin in experiment and observation can be explained to him, so that he may examine this and if necessary repeat the experiments and observations for himself. As a result he will then either decide to change his mind and confirm the decision or, on the contrary, decide to continue in his disagreement. Science, however, is built upon the fact that agreement is possible in a very large number of cases. Without such agreement science itself would be impossible.

Such considerations as these serve to demarcate the logic of the scientific method from other considerations which may be relevant to the pursuit of science, such as its psychology. It is also necessary to demarcate science from other branches of knowledge. This is fundamentally a question of adopting a particular convention. Conventions are matters for value judgments and can only be justified by their results. Positivists have taken verifiability as their criterion for the demarcation of science from metaphysics. But no scientific theory can be verified, in the sense of being shown to be true, and thus such a convention for demarcation would exclude science itself if applied strictly. It would throw out the baby with the bath water. Now the central problem which Popper wishes to eliminate from the logic of scientific knowledge, is the problem of induction. Inductive argument, as we have seen already, cannot be logically justified. "If A then B, and B" does not imply A. But an argument which can be applied, which *is* logically justifiable, is the argument known as "*Tollendo tollens*"—"By denying I deny". This argument is of the form "If A then B, but not B, therefore not A". The denial of a consequence of a theory *ipso facto* denies the theory from which it originated. Theories can thus be falsified although they can never be verified. Verifiability and falsifiability are, therefore, not symmetrical. Falsifiability is thus taken by Popper to be the criterion for the demarcation of scientific from metaphysical statements. Statements are scientific only in so far as they can be falsified. If those who insist upon verification are known as positivists, Popper might be called a negativist. The aims of science should be to negative hypotheses.

The theories and laws of natural science have the form of universal statements. A statement of this form would be, for example, "All swans are white". This would be a natural law concerning swans. Now such statements can never be shown to be true for, however long we searched, we could never be sure that we had examined all the swans that existed, and purple or black swans might still exist in spite of our searches. On the other hand, the discovery of a single specimen possessing a colour other than white would serve to refute the statement "All swans are white". This statement is equivalent to "There is no swan which is not white". The universal statement is equivalent to the negative of an existential singular statement.

On the other hand, existential singular statements such as "There exists a white swan" can be verified by the finding of a specimen of a white swan. At the same time such a statement cannot be falsified for the same reason that a universal statement cannot be verified. However long we searched we could never be sure that the statement "There exists a white swan" was false. A white swan might lurk in a corner we had not examined. Thus universal statements can be falsified but not verified whereas existential singular statements can be verified but not falsified. Each class of statement is unilaterally decidable only.

A scientific theory would be falsified if we decided to accept a basic statement which contradicts it, but it is necessary to put in one caveat. Basic statements will include some which refer to occurrences which are not reproducible. Such basic statements, although contradicting the theory, will not be taken as falsifying it.

Popper gives an analogy to help explain his position—an analogy with trial by jury. The jury's verdict "like that of the experimenter is an answer to a question of fact. ... The significance of this decision lies in the fact that from it, together with universal statements of the system (of criminal law) certain consequences can be deduced. In other words the decision forms the basis for the *application* of the system; the verdict plays the part of a 'true statement of fact'. But it is clear that the statement need not be true merely because the jury has accepted it. This fact is acknowledged in the rule allowing a verdict to be quashed.

"...In contrast to the verdict of the jury, the *judgment* of the judge is 'reasoned'; it needs and contains a justification. The judge tries to justify it by, or deduce it logically from, other statements: the statements of the legal system, combined with the verdict that plays the role of initial conditions."

The possibility of falsifying a theory will depend upon the nature of the theory. A theory is falsifiable according to the existential singular statements which it rules out. The theory that all swans are white is falsifiable because it rules out the existence of swans which are not white. The more a theory rules out the greater will be the possibility of falsifying it. Theories which rule out nothing are not falsifiable at all and are not scientific. A theory which rules out very little says very little. Such a theory would be difficult to falsify since, however most questions of fact came to be decided, the theory would still be conformable with them. On the other hand, a theory which rules out much, says much. It would be easy to falsify.

The programme of science thus consists in the continued attempt to falsify its theories. It is based upon a methodological decision never to shield a theory from falsification. On the contrary theories must be exposed to the process as fully as possible. A more readily falsifiable theory is to be preferred to one less readily falsifiable. All that can be said of a theory after the process has been carried out is that it has successfully withstood attempts to refute it so far. The process, however, has no natural termination, and its only termination is one which may be arbitrarily decided upon. It is always possible that further tests will result in the falsification of the theory, though at any given time and for the time being, it may be decided that the process has been carried as far as instrumental or other limitations will permit.

Popper's adoption of the *modus tollens* as the crux of the logic of science effectively removes the problem of induction from its epistemology. All the logical processes are deductive and thus subject to the ordinary rules of deductive logic. The question of how one is to proceed from singular to general statements does not arise. The removal of induction from the field of discussion not only removes the necessity to consider the possibility of arriving at truth by inductive processes but, at the same time, it also eliminates the question of arriving at probable truth in the same manner. Thus all the discussion of Bayes' theorem, connecting prior to posterior probability, also becomes unnecessary. This is not to say that questions of probability do not arise on the new view; they do, but they assume a quite different character than heretofore.

The question may, perhaps, be asked, how has all this been achieved? How can the perplexities which have withstood more than two hundred years of the closest examination, be removed at a single stroke? The strategy employed has been partly based upon methodological decisions and partly on rules for demarcation, both of which possess an element of arbitrariness. Have these decisions and demarcations succeeded in making the path of the logic of science clean by sweeping the problems into corners or under the carpet— places which we have decided not to explore? For example, the origin of the hypotheses from which the logic starts, is one such problem, and the decisions arising from experience is another. Both are ruled out from the logic of science by decisions of a conventional nature. They cannot be disposed of in this way. We simply agree to discuss one thing at a time and postpone them for discussion on another occasion.

Popper adopts a frequency definition of probability. We have seen how this leads to difficulties in assigning probabilities to hypotheses. The number of possibilities in the universe is infinite, so that if we attempt to define probability as a ratio of the number of favourable instances for the hypothesis to the total number of possibilities that exist, the result will either be zero or at best indeterminate. Popper, however, rejects inverse probability and Bayes' theorem as a basis for the scientific method. The theory of inverse probability seeks to show how the verification of the consequences raises the probable truth of a theory from which they are drawn. Popper selects an altogether different and practically contrary criterion to determine a figure of merit for a theory. He approaches the problem from the point of view of falsifiability. Since theories which have a good deal to say about the world of experience are more readily falsifiable than those which expose themselves less to experimental tests, it must necessarily follow that they possess a lower probability, *a priori*, of being true. A theory which said practically nothing about the world and which, therefore, was almost impossible to falsify would possess a very high probability of being true. On the other hand, such a theory would be virtually useless as a scientific theory. It seems, therefore, that we have to introduce a methodological rule that preference is to be afforded to theories which are most explicit, which rule out most, and which are therefore most open to falsification. This seems tantamount to the paradoxical decision to prefer those theories which possess the lowest probability of being true. Falsifiability and probability on Popper's view are bound to be complementary. As one increases the other will decrease.

The problem here involves the same question that was discussed in the previous chapter. To be useful for prediction a scientific theory must contain more than a logical construction of ascertained fact, or, to use the term employed in *The Logic of Scientific Discovery*, a construction out of agreed basic statements. Science progresses by testing the hypothetical residue left at any time in the content of a theory after such testing as has been carried out so far has corroborated the remainder. Without any hypothetical remainder a theory would not enable science to progress at all. At the same time any hypothetical residue will render the theory more liable to falsification and thus will have the effect of reducing its probability of being true. The greater the residue the greater will be this reduction. Now, though one can agree that scientific theories are valuable from the point of view of the development of science in so far, and only in so far, as they do contain such a residue of untested hypotheses, it is hardly true to say that this is the only criterion by which a theory should be judged. If such a doctrine were to be pushed to an extreme it would lead to the most elaborate and detailed hypothetical theories being preferred, even though no vestige of support could be found for their elaboration, beyond the bounds which those tests which had been carried out so far entailed.

Scientific theories, however, possess a descriptive as well as a predictive function. They should help us remember what we have discovered, by ordering it into a manageable system, as well as suggest further tests which could be carried out. It is the part played by scientific theories as descriptions of the world of experience which is in mind when scientific knowledge is under consideration. That such a descriptive function of scientific theories is necessary will become evident when we consider how new hypotheses are arrived at. This, as we have seen, has been placed by Popper outside the logic of science, but it is, nevertheless, of importance when deciding what a theory should aim to do. New theories cannot be advanced in a vacuum. Even when they replace an existing theory they have still to include those parts of the older theory where it has been successful. The human mind is incapable of grasping an extensive but unordered array of facts. It needs the help of an existing theory, giving even an imperfect pattern, to enable it to do so. For this purpose a theory which has successfully survived many attempts at falsification, or which has been well "corroborated", is required. As a theory survives attempts to refute it, the class of its potential falsifiers diminishes, and its probability increases, which, incidentally, is in close agreement with the previous views we have considered, such as those of Bayes, for example.

From the point of view of their descriptive merit the opposite choice, namely of theories possessing the highest degree of probability, would be made. Some moderator, therefore, seems necessary to the criterion of falsifiability, by which to judge a theory. A theory needs to say something more, but not a large amount more, than is justified by existing knowledge. It should not run too far in advance of experiment.

"And although I believe that in the history of science it is always the theory and not the experiment, always the idea and not the observation, which opens up the way to new knowledge, I also believe that it is always the experiment which saves us from following a track that leads nowhere: which helps us out of the rut and which challenges us to find a new way." (*L.S.D.*, p. 268.)

Theory and experiment are complementary arms which enable new territory to be conquered, and this would be beyond the capabilities of either alone. If they are to cooperate it is necessary that they keep in step and in close touch with each other. For this reason the greatest generality can only be gained from a base of theories of lesser generality, which have been already corroborated. The process is "quasi-inductive" to use Karl Popper's own expression.

Chapter XVII

ON UNDERSTANDING

How can we be said to secure an understanding of the world in which we live? Is such an understanding possible at all and if so in what sense can we be said to obtain an understanding of the world? All our imagery and language is couched in terms of our experience of the world. How can we use them to explain the world to ourselves and thus provide us with anything that merits the name of understanding? We cannot stand outside nature and thus refer it to a world beyond. We are part of the world of nature ourselves.

A large part of the behaviour of the animal kingdom is based upon inherited reactions. In many of the lower animals this process has attained a very high level of effectiveness indeed. The complicated behaviour of the social insects, for example, will come to mind in this connection. These animals are not equipped with very much in the way of brains; their nervous systems are dispersed over the body and only a series of nervous ganglia represent any accumulation of nervous tissue. The behaviour of these animals, which is often highly intricate, is automatic. Each species of bee lays its eggs in a nest which is characteristic of the species. The form is the same from one generation to another and can be foretold with certainty once the habit of the species is known. The previous generation is, as often as not, dead before the next appears and lessons in nest making are out of the question. Yet the same complicated routine is carried through to the letter, although any suspicion of understanding would appear to be unthinkable. The appearance of purposeful behaviour can, nevertheless, be very marked, as anyone who has been chased by a swarm of angry bees will testify.

Instinctive, automatic action remains an ingredient in the behaviour of the large-brained animals also. The moor-hen chick is able to swim the moment it first finds itself in the water. The foal is able to walk soon after it is born. The human infant breathes and cries and sucks without the necessity for lessons.

To secure a reward or to avoid punishment an animal can be trained to perform quite complicated series of operations. It can be got to repeat certain actions automatically by instilling them into it as a habit. Constant repetition can imprint a pattern into its behaviour. A horse can be trained to the rein or the heel so that it

163

reacts in a constant and predictable manner to stimuli administered in this manner. Its responses are reflex in nature and appear to afford no scope for mental processes of thinking. A dog may be trained in certain performances. At first it might appear that its tricks are performed in the conscious expectation of a reward. The delicacy it is to receive at the conclusion of the performance has to be on view from the beginning. But constant repetition can again render the responses automatic and the reward may be hidden and even never appear at all. Except for the initial stimulus which sets the action in train, its behaviour is as purely automatic as though it were instinctive. Like the horse the dog has then merely had a pattern stamped upon its behaviour. Birds which have been similarly trained in a complicated routine are used in the testing of drugs which affect the nervous system.

Though a large part of the behaviour of a dog may be explained on the basis of conditioned reflexes of this kind, it is possible that some element of conscious thought may make its appearance also. The excitement the animal shows on the appearance of its lead may well be nothing more than such a conditioned reflex action, as also may be the obvious satisfaction with which it greets the first aromatic indication of the appearance of its meal. It is well known that such action can be "conditioned" and be attached to other occurrences such as the ringing of a bell, which have been associated with its meal or the walk which it obviously enjoys. Human beings also react in a salivary manner to the smell of an appetising repast. The term reflex indicates that no mental activity is involved in the process which is like riding a bicycle, a thing we can do without taking thought. A dog will bring you its lead and pester you until you take it for a walk, or bring you a ball and pester you until you throw it for him. How far is such conduct the result of conscious thought, the result of some understanding of the situation?

In discussing the minds of animals we are brought up against the philosophical problem of "other minds". The philosophical problem is usually put as that of inferring other human minds from the behaviour of other people and the analogy of that behaviour with our own. We infer a toothache in another as a result of our own experience and the similarity of the behaviour we observe in the other to our own when we ourselves experienced a toothache. The possibility of inferring a mind in an animal is beset by all the same difficulties and, in addition, there is the dissimilarity between animal and human behaviour thrown in for good measure. All we have to go upon is their behaviour. They have no language with which they can tell us of their feelings or thoughts. The problem of animal minds lacks that helpful symmetry which induces a greater feeling of confidence into our thinking about the similar problem of the minds of other human beings.

Cats and dogs are content to spend long periods of time sleeping. What minds they possess obtain only occasional exercise. In contrast the apes are continually active and take an interest in everything they see. They can be set problems with which they can cope and in doing so they display an unmistakable, though still elementary, understanding of the situation. In his classical experiments with chimpanzees, Professor Köhler, who kept the animals in Teneriffe where they do well, tested their mental powers. He would put fruit, of which they were very fond, in front of their cages but out of reach by hand direct. He would provide sticks which could be used as tools to draw the fruit within reach. Finally he gave them bamboo sticks which were still too short to reach the prize, to see if they would insert one into the other to make a longer stick to achieve their purpose. The way of doing this was discovered at length by one of the apes and the series of experiments ended with one of them shaping a rod with his teeth to make it fit into the hole in another rod, an obvious example of purposive action based upon an understanding of the situation.

Chimpanzees will similarly pile boxes upon one another to make a ladder with which to secure fruit suspended out of reach. On one occasion the topmost box was placed by one ape with its open end upwards, thus contributing next to nothing to the height of the ladder. This mistake was never corrected. The ape climbed up the column and into the top box where it curled up comfortably and went to sleep. (*Minds of Animals*, *J. Arthur Thomson*, p. 93.)

The understanding shown by the apes was an understanding based upon the application of a new idea in a familiar situation. The use of a stick to extend the reach of the arm, the jointing of two sticks together to augment the length of a single one, the piling of boxes upon one another to increase the height attainable with one. The situation was seen in terms of something already familiar. An additional insight was required on each such occasion, such as the jointing of the sticks or the piling of the boxes, to provide a solution to the problem, but it was combined with existing knowledge.

Human behaviour, just as that of animals, possesses ingredients of an instinctive, acquired reflexive and mental nature. Some part, though no doubt a much smaller part than in the case of the animals, is instinctive. It is bred into us and is not acquired. Just how much there is of this kind is debatable and different estimates have been made by different philosophers. Are ideas of space and time instinctive, as was supposed by Kant, or are they acquired? Those with empiricist leanings would be reluctant to ascribe to instinct

12

that which could equally well be thought of as having been acquired. Though tests to distinguish between instinctive and other behaviour are conceivable with human beings they are not easy to carry out, and a range of view remains tenable. Others, such as Bergson, make a greater use of instinct. Until some test can be prescribed to differentiate between the two types of behaviour and to decide if and when learning takes place, the difficulty cannot be resolved. Of acquired habits of behaviour a great deal in the case of human beings, as with animals, is of the nature of reflex action. We balance ourselves, walk, ride bicycles and carry out all sorts of complicated actions without thinking. It is this, indeed, which makes life bearable. There are other things about which we are conscious of having to think and in which an understanding of a situation is involved. But what does understanding a situation entail? Does it necessarily comprise anything more than familiarity with the pattern of events, coupled with the assumption that the future will be conformable with the past?

A strictly empiricist position, which entails all knowledge being derived from the senses, leaves no room for anything but acquired knowledge. What we know of the external world comes about as a result of interpreting the various stimuli of which we are conscious. A child in its cradle learns to recognise a group of stimuli, always present together as a packet, as derived from an object in the external world. It learns the shape and colour of a ball from visual impression, the form and texture from tactual impressions, and impressions of taste, smell and hearing are often added as well. By assembling a number of such objects and noticing their mutual relationships mainly by means of the senses of touch and sight, the human child builds up his picture of the external world. As Bertrand Russell has remarked, it is an accomplishment which does great credit to the power of the infant mind. The empiricist position is certainly tenable and has, indeed, been held by a large number of English philosophers. Such involved ratiocination of the infant mind, however, seems rather less plausible, at any rate in any such extreme form, when it is remembered that a similar external world seems to be created by every human infant that is born reasonably healthy. The process brings to mind the instinctive behaviour of the wasp described by Fabre, which built its nest on his mantelshelf but, nevertheless, made the exterior an exact replica of the bark of the willow tree on which it normally builds, even though on the mantelpiece this surface tended to make the nest even more conspicuous than it otherwise would have been. If the construction of the external world by the human infant were really the result of a process of conscious reasoning one might imagine that from time to time minds which had reacted differently to their sensory stimulation would arise. This, however, does not seem to happen. The picture of an external world arises as automatically as the shape of the wasp's nest. Knowing the species they can be foretold in advance in either case. Such considerations point in the direction of Kant's "synthetic *a priori*"—knowledge about the world which we possess irrespective of the data of the senses. We would still wish to know how far the term knowledge would be applicable in such a case. Would a child born without any of its senses ever acquire knowledge even of time and space? The evidence provided by the learning to see of the congenitally blind would appear to indicate not. However, the universal picture of an external world could still arise as the result of an inherited reaction to the stimuli of the senses, fixed in the human species during the course of evolution because of its value for survival in the struggle for existence, just as the larva of the blow fly inherits an automatic avoiding reaction to the stimulus of light which its species has no doubt acquired in the same manner. The man born without senses would fail to react since he would be in receipt of no stimuli. The evolutionary advantage to a rational animal of a picture of the external world is obvious the moment we try to think without it, but it still leaves the nature of our knowledge of the external world an open question. It remains conceivable that a creature with a more effective mental image could arise and supplant the present race of men. Leaving aside such fantasies of the evolution of a race in which the multiplication tables were built in as hereditary equipment, and also, for the moment, the extreme empiricist view of knowledge, almost all that comes to us after the infant stage has, at present, to be acquired.

We become familiar in early childhood with the sequence of the natural numbers, 1, 2, 3, 4, etc. At a later stage we learn the series of the odd numbers, 1, 3, 5, 7, etc. and the even numbers 2, 4, 6, 8, etc. and reach the point of being able to recite these series without thinking. But if we are faced with the series, 1, 3, 7, 13, 21, 31, we would, for a time, be perplexed about how to go on. At length, however, the pattern would suddenly become clear and we would be able to exclaim with Wittgenstein, "Now I understand. Now I can go on." We would then be able to give the rest of the series, 43, 57, and so on. In this case the understanding has consisted in the recognition of a pattern. It was a pattern imposed by the originator of the series. When we were asked the question it was understood that the numbers did, in fact, possess some pattern and that all we had to do was to find it. It was assumed that the pattern presented by the numbers which had been given would continue to be followed as the series was extended and that the numbers were not a mere random selection.

The problem of seeing a pattern in nature is not quite the same. In no case have we any guarantee that what we observe possesses a pattern at all and is not just a random selection presenting the false appearance of pattern by chance. Neither have we any guarantee that the pattern so far observed will continue to rule the observations as their number is extended. It is quite possible that a limited series of numbers such as 1, 3, 7, 13, 21, 31, could be the result of chance and although we can, by searching, ascertain a rule they have followed so far, the next to turn up might well be 32.

It is among the presuppositions of science that a pattern exists in the phenomena of nature, which can be ascertained. Without some such assumption science, and indeed rational thought, would be impossible. One of the first stipulations which we make in a scientific investigation is that the results should be reproducible at will. In this way we hope to eliminate the possibility of an apparent pattern arising as the result of chance. This can never be certain. It is indeed possible that the same series of numbers, 1, 3, 7, 13, 21, 31, could arise by chance on every occasion when observations were made. This is, of course, another version of the difficulty which Popper solved by a methodological rule to eliminate improbable explanations. It is also similar to the difficulty of Hume. The conformability of the future to the past, which has so far been observed, might have been a matter of chance. As before we must put it on one side. It is necessary to assume that the pattern exists. It is only on this assumption that rational thought can be based.

On the basis of this assumption we can then face the question of how the pattern is to be discovered. In other words, how is an explanatory hypothesis to be arrived at—the question which is shelved in most current discussion centred on the hypothetico-deductive view of science. As Popper pointed out, this question is outside the purview of the logic of science. However, though it may belong much more to the psychology of the scientific method, it is none the less real and important for all that.

The mental powers of our friends the apes were limited. Nevertheless they were able to envisage a new problem in terms of the knowledge with which they were already familiar. The problems they faced had been specially posed for them by one with a superior intelligence. A solution existed though there was little reason to suppose that the apes themselves realised that a solution must exist for that reason. In this respect their problem was like the problem of the number series, though to them it would appear as a problem of the physical world appears to us—that is without a guarantee from any higher authority that a solution must exist.

Man's mental ability is also limited. How limited it is difficult to say, since we cannot remove the advantage which the possession of language gives us over the animals. However, in essence, man has perforce to employ methods similar to those adopted by the apes. He interprets the unfamiliar in terms of the familiar and compares the patterns presented by a new situation with those presented by the old. His explanations are in the nature of analogies and it is to the discussion of this character of scientific theories that a later chapter of this book will be devoted. While this view offers a fairly ready explanation of the origin of hypotheses, it also raises a number of problems. Is it to be expected that analogies can always be found? If they can be found is it to be expected that they will be capable of being applied to fields so far unexplored? Can they, in other words, furnish a basis for prediction? Can they offer a reliable guide to the nature of the physical world? Can they, that is, pretend to solve the riddle of the universe?

The answers to all these questions will turn out to be disappointingly largely negative. Nevertheless the process of advancing by means of analogies would appear to furnish an adequate description of what the activities of scientists actually are. Such a description may tend to emphasise the essential uncertainty of the scientific method and to assign to it only a very modest aim. At the same time it may exert a sobering influence on extravagant claims and induce a less dogmatic attitude, which, in many ways, is even more desirable than to find a solution to what is an essentially insoluble riddle.

Chapter XVIII

MODELS

The place occupied by mathematics in scientific theory has varied in the course of history. Since quite early times its place has been important, but the importance of the role it has played has oscillated in the course of time. It first occupied a central place in the views of the Pythagoreans, for whom all things were number. Then later, in astronomy, various more concrete physical pictures, such as rotating spheres, were adopted to account for the movement of the heavens. By the time of Ptolemy, however, they had become so complicated that they seemed to serve only as a vehicle to carry the mathematics. Prediction was dependent upon the disentanglement of the various harmonic constituents into which the observed movements were, in fact, decomposed. The central place occupied by geometry in mathematics rendered it necessary to associate them with the rotation of spheres in Ptolemy's theory of epicycles, but as observation improved the number of epicycles multiplied and by the time of the Alfonsine tables in the thirteenth century, the physical picture supporting the structure became more and more inadequate to the task.

The success of Copernicus lay more in the understandability of his picture of the universe than in the simplification he was able to introduce into the total scheme, which was, indeed, limited. It came to be felt that here was a theory which could be grasped and thought about. The development was continued by Galileo and Newton. In contrast to the makeshift models illustrating the Ptolemaic system, the Newtonian scheme, based on the material particle, was understandable and it could be pictured. Throughout the eighteenth century the theory of gravitation was worked out in immense detail without the sacrifice of any of the basic simplicity. It became the ideal upon which all scientific theories came to be modelled. The nineteenth century saw the proliferation of mechanical models and this was continued into the first quarter of the 20th. It would be a mistake to suppose that the mechanical models of the nineteenth century were always thought of as providing a picture of reality. More often they were parallel systems obeying the same laws as that being studied and thus giving rise to suggestions which could be investigated mathematically and put to the test of experiment. Thus a model of the aether suggested by Lord Kelvin consisting of steel rods, balls and gyroscopes did not give even the crudest picture of any real structure. It was merely an aid in the development of a mathematical calculus which could then be used to describe the phenomena directly. Maxwell's picture of vortices separated by freely revolving spheres was similar in nature.

With the advent of the electron, however, this position seems to have changed and the feeling grew that the model could be more than a mere parallel system useful as a basis for calculation. In atomic physics, however, in order to make the models fit the facts, it became necessary to make special assumptions departing from Newtonian mechanics and the classical theories of electricity based upon it. The theories became more and more mathematical and more and more difficult to picture, until in the matrix mechanics pictures were all but abandoned. The wheel came full circle and the situation became again very like that of the Ptolemaic theory of the universe.

In the course of these changes the Newtonian mechanics itself underwent modifications. The special theory of relativity improved the agreement between theory and observation though at some cost in increasing the mathematical complexity and reducing the possibility of intuitive manipulation. The general theory of relativity replaced the comparatively simple picture of a gravitational force by a curvature of space-time. This did not, however, succeed in supplanting the idea of force altogether since electrical force was not universal and differed according to the charge carried by a body. It could not be referred to a curvature of space. The new theory, therefore, remained a theory of gravitation, both curvature of space and force having to be retained. As far as the construction of mechanical models was concerned, however, the theory of relativity, though it contributed to the mathematical complexity of scientific theories, did not alter the situation fundamentally. It was, in essence, an elaboration of Newtonian theory, and mechanical models were found to break down even though they incorporated the relativistic modifications.

Models played a conspicuous part in the development of the theory of the atom. The earliest of the modern theories was the vortex theory of Lord Kelvin. It did not last long. It was an attempt to unify a theory of a universal aether and the atomic theory. It was the permanence displayed by vortex loops which appeared to make the idea attractive. After J. J. Thomson had produced his theory of the electron he elaborated a model of the atom in which electrons were embodied in a matrix of positive electricity, rather like a plum pudding. It also had a short life, proving inadequate to explain the facts. This was followed by the celebrated model constructed on the plan of a miniature solar system put forward by Lord Rutherford, on the basis of his experiments on the scattering of α particles. It was remarkable as being the first in which special *ad hoc* departures had to be made from the ordinary laws of mechanics and electricity, for, on the basis of accepted electrical theory, the model was unstable. It would have radiated energy until the planetary electrons had spiralled into the solar nucleus. The story is too well known to need repetition. Rutherford's model was adopted by Bohr, who, by means of his theory of stationary states, based his theory of spectra upon it. It achieved remarkable success in explaining the spectra of hydrogen and ionised helium, the two cases in which the mathematics involved proved tractable, but it was also elaborated by means of approximations so as to deal with more complicated cases. In this way, for example, it provided an explanation of the periodic table of the elements.

As an example of this kind of speculation and to give us something definite to criticise, let us consider the following extract from a paper by Rutherford on the structure of the atomic nucleus. It is taken from an address delivered to the Franklin Institute of Philadelphia on the occasion of their centenary in 1924. In this paper Rutherford indulges in speculation in a very free manner. There seems to be little doubt that his attitude was one of a very straightforward realism. He appears to have had little doubt that matter does in fact possess an understandable structure. There is little appearance of his intending only to formulate a mere scaffolding upon which a mathematical calculus embodying all the essential features of his theory, is to be constructed. He takes the nuclear atom for granted. He is simply casting about for the structure of the nucleus in simple mechanical terms, the existence of which he takes as established.

Rutherford first comments upon the similar nature of the decay of the "C" bodies in the uranium, thorium and actinium series of radio-active disintegration. He suggests that this may be due to the nuclei of these "C" bodies possessing the same central core, the differences in their properties being caused by differences in a satellite structure revolving round it.

He goes on:

In considering the satellite theory in connection with the radioactive bodies, it is at first sight natural to suppose, since the end product of both the radium and thorium series is an isotope of lead, that one of the isotopes of lead forms the central core. It may, however, well be that the radioactive processes cease when there are still a number of satellites remaining. If this be so, the core may be of smaller nuclear charge and mass than that of lead. From some considerations, described later, this core may correspond to an element near platinum of number 77 and mass 192.

. . . .

In concluding, I would like to make a few remarks of a more speculative character dealing with the fundamental problem of the origin and evolution of the elements from two fundamental building units, the positive and negative electrons. It must be confessed that there is little information to guide us with the exception of our knowledge of the nuclear charges and masses of the various species of elements which survive today. It has always been a matter of great difficulty to imagine how the more complex nuclei can be built up by the successive additions of protons and electrons, since the proton must be endowed with a very high speed to approach closely to the charged nucleus. I have already discussed in this paper the evidence that powerful attractive forces varying very rapidly with the distance are present close to the nuclear structure and it seems probable that these forces must ultimately be ascribed to the constituent proton. In such a case it may be possible for an electron and proton to form a very close combination, or neutron, as I have termed it. The probable distance between the centre of this doublet is of the order $3 \cdot 10^{-13}$cm. The forces between two neutrons would be very small except for distances of approach of this order of magnitude, and it is probable that the neutrons would collect together in much the same fashion as a number of small movable magnets would tend to form a coherent group held together by their mutual forces.

In considering the origin of the elements, we may for simplicity suppose a large diffused mass of hydrogen which is gradually heated by its gravitational condensation. At high temperatures the gas would consist mainly of free hydrogen nuclei and electrons, and some of these would in course of time combine to form neutrons, emitting energy in the process. These neutrons would collect together in nuclear masses of all kinds of complexity. Now the tendency of the groups of neutrons would be to form stable nuclear combinations, such as helium nuclei of mass four, and possibly intermediate stages of masses two and three. Energy would be emitted in these processes, probably in the form of swift surplus electrons which were not necessary for the stability of the system. In a sense, all these nuclear masses would be radioactive, but some of them in their transformation may reach a stable configuration which would represent the nucleus of one of our surviving elements. If we suppose that nuclear masses over a wide range of mass can be formed before serious transformation occurs, it is easy to see how every possible type of stable element will gradually emerge. If we take the helium nucleus as a combining unit which emits in its formation the greatest amount of energy, we should ultimately expect many of the neutrons in a heavy nucleus to form helium nuclei. These helium nuclei would tend to collect together and form definite systems and it seems not unlikely that they will group themselves into orderly structures, analogous in some respects to the regular arrangement of atoms to form crystals, but with much smaller distances between the structural units. In such a case, some of the elements may consist of a central crystal type of structure of helium nuclei surrounded by positive and negatively charged satellites in motion round this central core. Assuming that such orderly arrangements of helium nuclei are possible, it is of interest to note that the observed relations between atomic charge and atomic mass for the elements can be approximately obtained on a very simple assumption. Suppose that helium nuclei form a point centred cubic lattice with an electron at the centre of a crystal unit of eight helium nuclei. A few of the possible types of grouping are given in the following table, with the corresponding masses and nuclear charges. The structure 4.3.2. means a rectangular arrangement with sides containing 4,3,2. nuclei respectively. It will thus contain 24 helium nuclei, have a mass 96, and will contain 6 intranuclear electrons. Its nuclear charge will therefore be 48 − 6 = 42.

Structural arrangement of helium nuclei	Calculated nuclear charge	Calculated mass	Known element of equal charge
3.2.2.	22	48	Ti 48
3.3.2.	32	72	Ge 74, 72, 70
3.3.3.	46	108	Pd 106·7
4.2.2.	29	64	Cu 63·35
4.3.2.	42	96	Mo 96
4.3.3.	60	144	Nd 144
4.4.3.	78	192	Pt 195

While the agreement is far from perfect for all these structures, there is a general accord with observation. If we take the view that some of these structures can grow by the addition of satellites, there is room for adjustment of masses and to include the intervening elements. This point of view is admittedly very speculative and there may well be other types of structure involved. At the same time, the general evidence suggests that there are some basal structures on which the heavier atoms are progressively built up. The failure of the whole number rule for the mass of isotopes, observed in some cases by Aston, e.g., between tin and xenon, certainly supports such a conception. From a study of the artificial disintegration of the elements we have seen that carbon and oxygen represent very stable structures probably composed of helium nuclei. It is possible that oxygen nuclei, for example, may be the structural basis of some of the elements following oxygen, but our information is at present too meagre to be at all certain on this point.

. . . .

Rutherford here uses his wide experience of radioactivity to call attention to certain resemblances which he suspects might be significant. In attempting to systematise these observations he uses a scheme he already employed successfully in his theory of the outer atom and very familiar to him, to provide a structure for the nucleus. In the course of these speculations his fertile imagination constructs the neutron, not discovered until eight years later by Chadwick. Underlying all his speculation appears to be the firm conviction that nature can be understood in very simple terms. He is quite prepared to try a very crude picture of the nucleus on the lines of crystal structure, incapable of any searching test, and to make predictions from it about his central nuclear core.

Suppose that the idea of the crystalline core had been successful; what would it have indicated? Clearly nothing more is necessarily implied than that whatever regularities were exhibited by atoms happened also to be reproduced by the crystal model. We might even go further and ask what meaning can be attached to this supposed probing deeper and deeper into atoms, revealing structures hitherto unsuspected. As higher energies are employed for experiments new facts are likely to be brought to light. A supply of adjustable parameters is necessary with which to systematise them. The correlation of increasing energy with increasing complexity on a diminishing scale is capable of providing just this. It would be unwise to attach a deeper significance to the process than is implied by the convenience in systematising the observations, which it provides.

One of the most attractive features of Bohr's elaboration of the Rutherford model of the outer atom was the severe economy it preserved in adjustable parameters. His quantising condition, which was a new hypothesis, was only an extension of one already made by Planck. The assumption of the existence of stationary states, which violated both Newtonian and relativistic mechanics, was taken over from Rutherford. The emission of radiation in electron jumps was parallel to the behaviour which Planck had assumed for his oscillators, as was the relation between the frequency of the radiation and the energy emitted. Without further assumptions, the Rydberg universal spectroscopic constant was given in terms of constants already known—the electronic charge and mass and Planck's constant of action. With regard to atoms of higher atomic weight whose atomic spectra were more complicated the theory gave valuable qualitative rather than quantitative results.

Yet the theory had serious defects which proved difficult to remedy. It was not altogether self-consistent. Half quantum numbers had had to be invoked in some cases and more complicated ones in others. These were necessitated by experiment but had no theoretical foundation. Other *ad hoc* assumptions, such as the Exclusion Principle of Pauli and the spinning electron, were introduced, for which the theory provided no basis. There were also a few phenomena connected with the spectra of hydrogen and ionised helium for which the theory proved inadequate. No means, other than by borrowing

results from classical theory, were available for calculating intensities
or polarisations of the lines of the spectra and the same could be
said of the so-called forbidden energy drops.

Bohr's theory of the atom has now been superseded but it played
an essential part in the gradual evolution of atomic theory. Subsequent developments have shown that a satisfactory atomic model
could not be constructed out of the familar concepts which Rutherford and Bohr employed. Evolution has been in the direction of
increasing abstraction. Familiar concepts, which proved inadequate
for the purpose, have been replaced by mathematical symbolism.
The aim has become to construct a calculus which can be employed
for prediction rather than a model by which the atom could be
pictured. We must trace these developments briefly to see where they
have led us, though it will be possible to do so only in the merest
outline.

In an attempt to remove some of the arbitrariness in Bohr's
quantum theory, de Broglie put forward his wave theory. The
stationary states of the atom then found a natural explanation in
terms of stationary vibrations, similar to those of a bell or plate,
which oscillate only at certain definite frequencies. His object was
thus to improve the model and make it more intelligible by employing
a wave rather than a particle picture. Taking the photon interpretation of light as a guide he associated a particle of rest mass m_0,
moving with a velocity v, with a wave of frequency v and velocity V
given by

$$W = hv \quad \text{and} \quad p = hv/V$$

p being the relativistic expression for the particle's momentum.

It follows that

$$V = \frac{W}{p} = \frac{c^2}{v}$$

The waves move much faster than the particle, indeed much
faster than light. This, however, is unobjectionable because the
energy of the waves is transmitted with the particle velocity, not the
wave velocity. In the wave picture a field of force becomes a distribution of refractive index so that the waves are refracted. The
transmission of energy with the velocity of the particle becomes its
propagation by means of a wave packet travelling with the group
velocity of the waves. The mechanical problem of determining the
trajectory of a particle is thus equivalent to the determination of the
propagation of a wave packet.

The association of wave properties with matter by de Broglie was
a shot in the dark but it was soon justified by experiments by Davisson

and Germer, G. P. Thomson and others. It was de Broglie's hope that the waves would prove to be the fundamental reality of nature, particle manifestations being approximations, the two being similar to wave and ray optics, respectively.

De Broglie's waves formed the basis of Schrödinger's wave theory of the atom. De Broglie had treated the stationary states of the atom by means of what may be described as ray optics. An electronic orbit would correspond to a stationary state if it contained a whole number of wavelengths. Such a view proved incapable, however, of providing a detailed theory of the atom, and Schrödinger's advance was to replace de Broglie's ray treatment by wave theory. It was as a more precise model that the theory was first developed. Thus it was felt to be no objection that the wave optics did not specify definite electronic orbits; the wave picture was the correct one, that of particles an approximation. The success of the theory was immediate. Stationary states lost their arbitrariness, optical frequencies in the spectra became difference frequencies between stationary modes of vibration, the correspondence principle followed from the theory and was not something imposed ad hoc, intensities and polarisations were calculable unambiguously and difficulties over forbidden transitions and half quantum numbers were removed. Nevertheless success was bought at a price of a considerable increase in abstraction.

In Schrödinger's early theory of the hydrogen atom the waves determined the distribution of charge in a "charge cloud". In the simple case of the hydrogen atom with the nucleus assumed at rest, this could be treated as real. The system possesses three degrees of freedom and the de Broglie waves are capable of being represented in three-dimensional space. With systems possessing more than three degrees of freedom, however, Schrödinger's treatment required a space of more than three dimensions for the description of the charge cloud. A space of more than three dimensions is obviously a mathematical fiction and what reality can be attached to something which can only be represented in a fictitious space is problematical. The three-dimensional problems became special cases where the difficulty was obscured without being removed. A further difficulty occurred over the wave packet. It was shown that the behaviour of such a packet would be to disperse and the dispersal would take place very rapidly so that the particulate nature of the electron would be lost.

That physical reality could not be assigned to de Broglie waves was obvious on other grounds also. When a beam of radiation falls upon a surface part of it is reflected and part transmitted. The wave theory depicts this on the basis of the reflection and transmission of waves. The corresponding particle picture depicts it as a cloud of particles some of which are reflected and some transmitted. The intensities of the transmitted and reflected waves corresponded to the number of particles supposed to make up these beams on the particle theory. Now consider one of these particles only, in the cloud. It may be reflected or it may be transmitted. It cannot be both and the intensities of the two waves corresponded to the probability of reflection or transmission of the particle taking place. Let us proceed now to the case of an isolated electron striking the face. There is a certain chance that it will be reflected and another that it will be transmitted. Suppose a fluorescent screen to be interposed in the path of the possible reflection and that a scintillation occurs. It is then known that the particle has been reflected. The chance of its having been in the transmitted beam is thereby reduced to zero. The intensity of the transmitted wave must therefore suddenly vanish as the result of an occurrence which may have taken place at a remote distance. If the waves merely represent the probability of finding the electron in the reflected or transmitted beams, this is of no consequence. Probabilities depend upon our knowledge of the situation. On the other hand, such a point of view divests the waves of any claim to possess an independent material existence.

Such a view of the nature of Schrödinger's waves came to be forced on physicists by the nature of events. The waves had to be looked upon as mathematical expressions defining the probability of finding an electron at any point, an interpretation first put forward by Born. However useful the idea of a wave may be in aiding the manipulation of the formulae, if pressed we have to remember that basically all that we have is a mathematical calculus to which it has so far been possible to tie experience, without reasons being forthcoming which would explain why this should be so.

Just as wave optics predicts a limit to the sharpness of any optical image, so the wave mechanics predicts a limit to the sharpness with which the momentum and position of an electron can be specified. This is the basis of the celebrated principle of uncertainty of Heisenberg. Just as in the case of a photographic image the grain of the film usually sets the limits of sharpness and only with refined instruments are the limits of optical resolution attained, so in the case of the observations of physics, it is the errors of observation which normally limit the accuracy rather than the uncertainty indicated by the quantum theory, and it is only in refined observations that these limits are encountered. Nevertheless the principle of uncertainty cuts at the root of causality and determinism. Macroscopic events, which depend upon large numbers of microscopic events, remain practically completely determined, as before. It is the micro-

scopic events which can only be predicted with a measure of probability. One of the principal aims of any scientific theory must be to
predict the future and this applies to the quantum theory no less than
to any others. Underlying the term probability is, as we have seen,
the idea that the future will be conformable to the past. The half
life of radium is a constant which can be measured accurately although individual disintegrations cannot be forecast. The principle
of uncertainty aroused interest partly because of its possible effects on
the problem of free will. The uncertainty of microscopic events
might provide an avenue through which the mind could act on
matter. This is perfectly true, but the position is not fundamentally
changed from what it was. The problem of whether the mind can
affect the probability of microscopic events and through them,
macroscopic events, is exactly the same as the problem of whether
the mind is capable of altering the normal behaviour of matter.

The final step in abstraction was taken in the development of the
matrix quantum mechanics. Though its results are identical with
those of the wave mechanics interpreted as dealing with probability
waves, its origin and structure are entirely different. It starts with
the principle that only entities which can be observed, at least in
principle, should enter into a physical theory. It thus has this in
common with the simple operational analysis of nineteenth century
chemistry given in Chapter XV. It belongs to the phenomenological
school of philosophy. In the matrix quantum mechanics there is no
mention of electrons in orbits or of quantum jumps. Frequencies,
intensities and polarisations can be measured accurately, while the
motion of the electron in Bohr's theory plays no direct part in the
processes of radiation. If we can construct our theory in terms of the
former and exclude the latter we would be wise to do so. However
we have already seen that a theory which limits itself to constructs
out of observables is useless for prediction. The "observables"
which enter into the matrix theory are selected with a good deal of
sophistication. In addition to the frequency, intensity and polarisation of the emitted radiations, the energy levels of the atom are
claimed to be observable and even the question of phase enters into
the theory. Atomic fields of force have also to be assumed.

Matrix mechanics forms a stage more complex than wave mechanics. It operates with matrices of special type in a Hilbert space of
infinite dimensions. In this the wave mechanics might appear to
possess an advantage but it has to be remembered that wave
mechanics also operates in a multi-dimensional space and is fundamentally unpicturable. Both are mathematical calculi capable of
codifying experience in considerable detail and they are equally
successful. From our present point of view what the new mechanics

demonstrates is that the physical pictures of the circulating electrons in the Bohr atom can be dispensed with and the fact that the success of the new mechanics extends beyond that attained by Bohr indicates that it is necessary to do so. Indeed, if we are pressed we are bound to reject the picture in which the theories originated as being inadequate for the purpose which it attempts to serve, and to fall back upon the mathematical abstractions of the later theories.

What logical status can we ascribe to these mathematical calculi? It would make no sense to say that they are a direct description of an inferred universe which is hidden from us, which the older picturable theories claimed to do. At best they are a description of the quantities admitted by Heisenberg into his category of observables. It would have no meaning to ask whether or not the theories are true, or even probably true in some inner fashion. The only sense in which they can be said to be true is that they have so far furnished correct predictions. We study the phenomena we study directly and not some hidden world beyond. Such a hidden world may or may not exist. Our task is to correlate the phenomena which we are able to observe.

In spite of their limitations, however, models have by no means vanished from the scientific scene. They still retain a usefulness for limited purposes. In thinking of the Compton effect, for example, the idea of collisions between electrons and photons still gives a good quantitative account of what happens. In chemistry, models in the simpler sense of formulae or even constructional units are still employed and it would be foolish to complicate a situation unnecessarily by using a more complicated model than the circumstances require. The results of the kinetic theory of gases can be obtained from the use of the billiard ball model of the molecule. These models furnish, of course, a description of limited accuracy only and their use requires a knowledge of their limitations or they may be used out of context. A theory built upon them is useful only for certain purposes. Indeed the same must be true of the more complicated wave and matrix mechanics themselves. It is highly improbable that even if they were completely satisfactory today they will remain unaltered in the future. Phenomena will, no doubt, be discovered which will entail their modification. Should such modification be made at the cost of greater complication, then the present theories would, almost certainly, be retained to deal with the present range of facts, the new phenomena being regarded as being out of context for the mechanical methods of the present time.

This implies a view of the aim of scientific models which is more limited than would have been at one time taken to be the case. If they aim at only a correspondence with experience within a limited field then the discovery of a recalcitrant fact is no longer capable of destroying a beautiful theory. All that it does is to limit the context in which the picture is applicable. The theory and the phenomena have only a limited number of aspects in common. In other words they form analogies rather than complete descriptions. We are again led to much the same conclusion as we reached at the end of the last chapter. We must now examine this idea in a little more detail.

Chapter XIX

SCIENTIFIC THEORIES AS ANALOGIES

We have already seen how an element of metaphysics has played an important part in getting scientific theories accepted. Any analysis of the scientific method, however, is bound to attempt to distinguish between the physical and metaphysical content. In this, attention must be directed to the question what in scientific theories may be looked upon as knowledge and something of the attitude of positivism adopted. Considered simply as tools for further investigation scientific theories often appear to present an inextricable mixture of the well founded and the hypothetical—which may or may not turn out to be justifiable—which is incapable of being sorted out. In this chapter the view will be developed that this is not an essential feature of science and that theories can function both as summaries of knowledge which has been acquired and also serve as tools for further research if the purpose of science is looked upon as the development of analogies rather than an approach to absolute "truth".

Even in the approach to the scientific method in the theory of inverse probability arising out of Bayes' theorem, which is usually couched in terms of establishing the truth of the hypothesis through the confirmation of deductions from it, we have seen how Jeffreys' theorem concerning repeated confirmation, demonstrates that the success of scientific prediction is to be expected whether the hypothesis from which it arises, is true or false. Confirmation of a hypothesis, therefore, cannot remove its metaphysical content, as is, indeed, otherwise obvious. Metaphysics has played a large part in the history of science and no doubt still does in activating individuals in the pursuit of research, but it need not be built into the structure of scientific belief itself. The objection that positivism cannot provide theories which are "open ended" and thus raise subjects for future enquiry and serve as useful guides for research, cannot be maintained if for the object of science is taken the more modest aim of the development of analogies. Analogies can be both heuristic and mnemonic whilst the object of an analysis of the process must be to distinguish between that part of the analogy which has been shown to be positive and that which for want of investigation may turn out to be positive or negative when it comes to be examined. The metaphysical element is removed when the theory is used as an analogy rather than as a direct description of inner truth.

In order to examine the possibility of looking upon scientific theories as analogies it may be helpful to proceed from a very simple concrete example. For this purpose the very elementary theory of electricity is a convenient one to take. The theory of electricity has been worked out as completely as any theory in science and it is based upon a few simple concepts. The present basis of these concepts lies, of course, in modern accurate measurements, but they originated in comparatively crude observations which have been refined as time has gone on. We shall have no need, however, to trace these developments very far to enable us to accomplish our purposes. These will be served by an examination of the justification for conceiving an electric current as a flow of something. In elementary courses the necessity for justifying this at all is more often overlooked than not. "The word current is so expressive in common language that when applied in the consideration of electrical phenomena we can hardly divest it sufficiently of its meaning or prevent our minds being prejudiced by it." Here, as so often is the case, the use of a common word serves only to obscure the problem involved.

The idea of electric current developed gradually in the course of the study of electrostatics. At first electric charge was explained on the basis of electric "effluvia" emanating from charged bodies. The tingling sensation when a charged body is held close to the face—now explained on the basis of attractions acting on the hairs of the skin—was taken as evidence supporting the concept. In so far as it placed the emphasis on the space surrounding the body, rather than on the body itself, it had certain affinities to modern field theories. The theory of effluvia, however, later became replaced by theories assuming an electric fluid residing in the charged body itself—at first a two-fluid theory followed by one of a single fluid, to which later had to be added the concept that ordinary matter was self-repellent in order to explain the repulsion which negatively charged bodies exerted on each other. On the fluid theory of electricity the discharge of charged bodies came then to be looked upon as a flow of the electric fluid or charge from one body to another, and this gave rise immediately to the concept of the electric current.

After Oersted had demonstrated the action of an electric current on a magnet and Ampère the action of one current upon another, it was generally assumed that the force experienced by a magnetic pole or another current, when placed near an electric circuit, was proportional to the strength of the current to which the force was due. Since there was no other accurate way by which the current could be measured this amounted to a completely new definition of the meaning of the word current, which thus became equivalent to a quantity proportional to the magnetic force which was observed under fixed geometrical conditions. When such a shift of definition is made it becomes imperative, of course, to ensure that the new way of looking at the quantity concerned is capable of fitting the older views arising from what is essentially an entirely different conception.

The new view of the electric current can be seen more easily from the classical apparatus designed by Ohm to elucidate his well-known law. To measure his currents Ohm suspended a small magnet just above one of his conductors which he arranged to run in the north–south direction. He did not, however, allow his magnet to be deflected by the current in the conductor but brought it back to its original position by means of a twist applied to a torsion wire supporting the magnet, when the current was switched on. It is of interest to notice, in passing, that in this way Ohm had shown his appreciation of the necessity to keep the distance between his conductor and the magnet constant. It was this quantity—the twist necessary to be applied to the torsion wire—to which Ohm's law applies. The word current is clearly not justifiable at this stage.

The new procedure raises immediately the question of what it is that is being measured. It is, of course, nothing more than the magnetic effect of whatever is happening in the conductor. What does this indicate? Many observations that would appear to be obvious and scarcely to need examination on the view that a current of something is flowing, in fact need to be carefully tested. Of course, even if there is a current of something flowing, it is not known what this something is. It is not known whether it is indestructible or whether it is capable of being converted into some form of energy such as heat or light, for example. Certain tests are really equally necessary even on the view of the flow of a current, but the change to the magnetic method of measurement brings out the difference. It is not, for example, obvious *a priori*, that similar measurements made at various points of the same circuit will give the same result. This is the result of an observation that can only come from experiment. Even if it is assumed that the measurement of the magnetic effect gives a measure of a current flowing, the result would still not be obvious since it would be possible for the electric current to disappear when it passes through a resistance and generates heat. The continuity of the electric current as measured by the magnetic effect, all the way round the circuit, is one of the most important facts in the study of electric currents. Upon it depends the calibration of one instrument in terms of another, than which, perhaps, no more fundamental measurement exists in the science. Experiments to test this were, in fact, carried out by Ampère, who suspended magnets over a conductor connected to an electric pile and over the pile itself, and he observed equal deflections in the two cases. Ampère's observations were of the crudest, but in spite of the fundamental importance of the law in question no one seems to have thought it necessary to repeat them at the standard of modern measurement.

Similarly Kirchoff's first law, that when an electric circuit divides the algebraic sum of the "currents" in the branches which meet at a point is zero, is also not obvious *a priori*. Whatever ideas may have been held about the electric fluid, it would certainly not appear obvious that the sum of the magnetic effects observed in the separate branches would add, algebraically, to zero. Kirchoff's first law is thus also empirical and cannot be arrived at by a process of reasoning alone. It might, perhaps, be suggested that the law could be made analytical by employing it in the calibration of current measuring devices. Thus the two ampere readings might be marked on one instrument by connecting it to two other instruments each giving a reading of one ampere, in such a way that both the one-ampere currents were made to flow through the first instrument. Such a procedure merely shifts the difficulty without solving it. If this plan is adopted it would be necessary to call in question the proportionality between current and magnetic effect which it would be necessary to establish afresh experimentally. The necessity for experiment would be simply transferred to a neighbouring field.

It has been necessary to make these points at the risk of appearing to labour them because, armed with the two experimental results— namely, the continuity of the magnetic measurements round a circuit and Kirchoff's first law—it is then possible to commence the formulation of an analogy between the electric "current" as indicated by the magnetic effect, and the flow of a fluid, such as water, in a continuous circuit of pipes. Two things are analogous when they possess certain properties in common. The value of an analogy is two-fold. In the first place it helps us to remember what we have discovered. In the present case we liken the behaviour of electricity, with which we suppose ourselves to be unfamiliar, to that of water in pipes, with which we suppose that we are already familiar. In the second place the analogy suggests further things which we might proceed to test. An analogy will be more valuable the greater its extent. If only one or two properties are shared by the two members of the analogy, it would hardly be worth putting forward. On the other hand, if the correspondences are numerous, then it becomes a valuable aid to thinking. We are able to say that for many purposes which can be enumerated, that which is being investigated behaves *as if* it were the same as the familiar member of the analogy. We can imagine an electric current as a fluid flowing in a pipe.

The analogy can be extended beyond the simple limits to which we have so far taken it. The rate at which work has to be done to maintain a flow of water in a pipe is given by the product of the quantity of water flowing per unit time and the pressure difference produced by the pump maintaining the flow. There is a corresponding interpretation in the electrical case involving the electric current and the electromotive force, the latter being defined in terms of the rate of working to correspond to the pressure difference in the water. Pipes and conductors can also be related according to the resistance they offer to the flow of water in the first case and electricity in the second. The resistance in the case of a water pipe may be defined to be the pressure difference required to cause a unit current of water to flow along the pipe, and that of a conductor to electricity as the electromotive force required to generate unit electrical current in the conductor.

It is not possible, however, to extend the analogy indefinitely, and if this is attempted a limit is soon reached. As an example, take the case of resistance. The resistance of a wire towards a current of electricity is proportional to its length and inversely proportional to its area of cross section. The resistance of a pipe to the flow of water is also proportional to its length, as in the case of the electric current, but unlike the case of the electric current, it is inversely proportional not to the area of the cross-section but to the square of this quantity instead. Again, any electrical fluid which may exist possesses no inertia apart from the effects of self-induction, as may be shown by the absence of an induced electromotive force on switching on or off a current in a wire doubled back along itself. A water current, on the other hand, doubled back along itself does possess inertia and will continue to flow after the driving pressures have been removed. Similarly, the Bernoulli effect, by which a current of water can be made to flow against a pressure gradient, as it flows from a place where the water is moving quickly to one where it is moving slowly, has no counterpart in electricity. There is also the obvious fact that in the case of a current of water there is no counterpart to the magnetic field which surrounds an electric current.

The analogy is limited and if it is to be used at all it is essential that the limits should be understood; otherwise the theory will be applied out of context. The fluid theory of electricity can be further extended by looking upon the fluid as being composed of electrical particles. In this way the phenomena of electrolysis and the experiments of Millikan can be brought within the scope of the analogy. Such an analogy, however, again breaks down in the case of the conduction in metals where it is necessary to assume that a wave character is possessed by the electrical particles. A gas is, in many ways, analogous to a cloud of swiftly moving material particles, the closeness of the analogy depending upon the degree of sophistication introduced into the model. Again a limit is reached, as for example, where the expected equipartition of energy among the particles fails to correspond to the behaviour of the gas.

There would appear, thus, to be much to be said in favour of regarding scientific theories as analogies. It relieves the theorist of the difficulty of having to say that an electric current *is* a flow of electrons, or that a gas actually consists of a cloud of swiftly moving molecules. He has need to do nothing further than to say that for certain specified purposes the electric current behaves *as if* it were a flow of electrons or that certain of the properties of a gas are the same *as if* the gas were composed of swiftly moving molecules. He is in fact, of course, never entitled to say more on any view of the scientific method which can be maintained. It also relieves him of the necessity of having to produce always a theory which is complete. A wave particle duality may be unfortunate but there is no reason why we should not employ particles on Mondays, Wednesdays and Fridays, and waves on Tuesdays, Thursdays and Saturdays, so long as we are aware of the extent and the limitation of each analogy.

The analogy thus reproduces the essential features of a scientific theory. In the first place it is capable of playing the role of a summary of experience, which is probably the principal purpose which a scientific theory has to fulfil. It also enables a calculus to be invented by means of which experience can be brought within the reach of rational thought. It differs from the more common view of the nature of a scientific theory in two ways. It is commonly thought that scientific theories furnish predictions and also that it is the predictions which are capable of furnishing criteria by means of which the theories may be tested. An analogy cannot predict anything new. Because two things possess certain properties in common there is not the slightest reason to suppose that any other property possessed by one of them will also be shared by the other. Any such property may well lie beyond the limits of the analogy. On the other hand, the analogy does suggest further lines of enquiry in order that it may be extended as far as is possible. There is not the slightest guarantee, *a priori*, or indeed even probability, that any given extension is possible. It can only be explored to find out.

Yet predictions are made in which we place the utmost confidence. The Nautical Ephemeris contains tables giving with great accuracy the positions which the heavenly bodies will occupy in the future. Everyone accepts them and is prepared to risk his life upon their accuracy by entrusting himself to ships and aeroplanes navigated by their means. We cross a bridge built by engineers in the utmost confidence that it will not collapse underneath us. We may even decide upon the desirability of a picnic on the basis of the weather forecast. The basis of the predictions of the astronomers is the previous motion of the heavenly bodies. This motion has been analysed into a series of harmonic cycles which have been repeated for at least as long as observations have been made. The engineer relies upon past experience with materials and he expects these properties to continue. The weather forecaster relies on the repetition of previous weather patterns. The analogy which all these sciences employ is that between the future and the past. Upon this, as we have seen, we must perforce rely. The same conclusions apply to scientific laws which are simply explicit statements about past experience. Even this coherence of the future with the past is open to Humean doubt. The situation is different when we explain the behaviour of an electric current as being due to a flow of electrical particles. Past experience is then that in certain respects the electric current and a flow of electrically charged particles have certain properties in common. Unless we are prepared to maintain on the basis of limited experience that the two are identical, and this would clearly be quite unjustifiable, we cannot deduce anything about the likelihood of further properties being shared. We know in this case that the analogy is limited. Certain phenomena can only be explained if the electric current possesses a wave structure.

This view of scientific theories as analogies mirrors more accurately the actual activities of the scientist than does the idea of a prediction. If there was any measure of certainty that a prediction would be correct, the necessity to test it would appear much less urgent than it is. Scientists commonly display no noticeable confidence in their predictions. Every one of them is submitted to the most stringent tests that can be devised as soon as they can be carried out. In accordance with the views of Professor Popper, every effort is made to falsify the theory. To look upon this process as the extension of an analogy indicates no unjustified expectation of success.

The demand that effort should be concentrated on attempts to falsify a theory is replaced, on the view that theories are analogies, by the demand that the analogy should be extended if possible and delineated. The limits of an analogy can only be determined in one particular at a time. Whether it is looked upon as falsifying a theory or delineating an analogy, the direction of scientific effort is much the same in either case. In using an analogy, however, we are naturally careful only to employ it within the limits within which it has been tested. It has no currency outside.

We have already mentioned that at one time it was thought

that a single contrary instance could destroy a theory. Popper's demand for falsification would eliminate theories in this way. With some little modification, however, most of them seem well enough able to manage to survive! We have also become accustomed to accepting what were thought to be diametrically opposite views at the same time, or rather to taking them as alternative explanations applicable to the same thing in different fields, a situation which is not fundamentally altered by the invention of a calculus which can comprehend both views in one set of formulae. On the other hand, if scientific theories are no more than analogies, then clearly we are able to employ the most convenient one for the purpose in hand. What we are studying is the phenomena of nature. The theory merely enables us to pursue this quest systematically.

Looking upon a scientific theory as an analogy also offers no unwarranted belief in the ultimate truth of its picture or of the objective existence—whatever may be meant by that term—of the entities it postulates. Science has no necessity to insist upon the fundamental veridity of the pictures it proposes, whether concrete, as in the fashion of the last century, or in the mathematical mode of the present. Such questions, of course, cannot be decidable by scientific methods and lie beyond the province of science. This is not to deny that many may experience feelings of the strongest conviction when faced with the phenomena of nature and the explanations which science offers for them. In the same way no doubt a similar conviction was felt in the middle ages about the intelligences which were then invented to keep the heavens in motion. It is not, however, necessary for science to insist on anything more than that within certain limits matter behaves *as if* it was built in a certain way. There seems everything to be said in favour of this more modest claim.

The term analogy can only occur at a level of discourse which accepts the concepts of properties possessed by permanent objects. There will, therefore, be questions concerning the theory of knowledge which cannot be appropriately raised at this level. This does not mean, of course, that these problems are in any way pseudo, for as we have seen problems cannot be solved by adopting the simple expedient of employing a language in which they cannot be expressed.

An analogy, for example, can exist between two single things; they can possess certain properties in common. Since it is possible to examine each of them individually such an analogy can be established by a logically valid argument in the *modus ponens*. A and B possess a property P in common. They are, therefore, analogous in respect to this property. Strictly speaking this could

13*

only be asserted of A and B at a particular instant—the instant at which the properties were examined. It does not follow that because they both possessed the property P at this time they will both continue to possess it at a later time. The properties of either or both might change in the interval. The usefulness of the idea of an analogy can only be apparent when bodies and properties are fairly permanent. The problem of the persistence of properties is thus not solved but rather shelved in talking about analogies in this way.

A similar argument may be applied to analogies between members of limited classes, which can be exhaustively examined. However, we run into the usual difficulties when classes have to be dealt with which are too big to deal with exhaustively. These are the same problems as are attached to the difficulty of generalisation. We cannot measure all the possible values of the pressure and volume of a gas, and yet we have every confidence that we know the relation between them on the basis of a comparatively few sample readings. On this basis we feel content to build the analogy with the cloud of molecules. The language we use in speaking of an analogy in such a case assumes that a gas possesses such ascertainable properties, in the same way as such properties are assumed in Professor Popper's basic sentences. On the other hand we do not avoid the difficulty inherent in generalisation by concentrating our attention on falsification, though it is on this that we do in fact concentrate. We do not waste our time in a vain attempt at measuring every conceivable pressure and volume in a certain range. Rather we seek to falsify the theory by proceeding to other ranges. We seek, in other words, to extend the analogy, for example, by seeing if there is anything to correspond to the volume of the molecules composing the cloud. In doing this we are simply assuming that the difficulties of generalising can be surmounted.

As a science progresses the area which is looked upon as being "understood" expands. The patterns in the new areas become familiar and, in their turn, they become capable of acting as the familiar side of a new scientific analogy, dealing with some fresh phenomenon. In this way the degree of sophistication of a science continually increases. For an analogy to be useful, however, it is essential that the properties of one member of it should be familiar. An artificially constructed analogy formed from bodies which possess only those properties which are necessary for the theory, is subject to the same limitations as the theory built up from logical constructs. It is not suggestive. The molecules of which our gas may be looked upon as being composed, must possess some of the properties of macroscopic bodies. It must be possible for them to possess volume, for example, although in the initial formulation of the theory this found no application. There must be further properties to be examined if the theory is to be alive and grow. A theory which has ceased to grow, however, is by no means useless. Its function then becomes purely descriptive and this is valuable in itself. It was this function of a scientific theory which occupied the central place in the older considerations of the scientific method. It is also essential if the theory is to form the familiar side of a new analogy in some other developing field.

Chapter XX

CONCLUSION

We have, in the course of this book, touched upon four different views of the nature of the scientific method. These were first the view arising out of the considerations of probability, connected with the theorem of Bayes and the Rule of Succession, second the view of a scientific theory as a logical construction out of observables, third the view of the sciences as processes of falsification of hypotheses tentatively put forward and fourth as descriptions of nature by analogy. The first is an attempt to see how far science can arrive at an answer to the cosmological problem—it envisages an ultimate approach to "truth". The second concentrates upon the limitations of scientific concepts and seeks to determine how much real knowledge they contain, the third deals with theory as a tool for further exploration and the fourth as a means of learning about and systematising the phenomena of nature. Let us in conclusion, attempt to summarise our findings and see how far each can take us in the direction in which it attempts to lead.

As far as considerations of probability are concerned, there would appear to be nothing amiss with the mathematical calculus which the theory has erected. It has stood the test of two centuries of critical examination successfully, so that the calculus itself, which is distinct from the theory which gave rise to it, seems likely to be completely reliable. It is, moreover, applied with complete success in many of the calculations of the everyday world. We have seen further, that Bayes' theorem is capable of being applied successfully to the consideration of the probability of certain scientific theories. The question which finally requires to be examined is how far such cases can be taken as exemplifying the working of the scientific method in general.

If we are to accept the solution of the problem of science as furnished by the frequency theory of probability, it is necessary that the number of alternative theories should be limited and that we should be able to estimate their probabilities. If the problem is bounded in this way, then the theory shows that science may be able to approach "truth" asymptotically. The difficulty in thus limiting the problem, as well as in accepting the frequency theory, however, is formidable, and it is difficult to see how it may be surmounted in the general case, though there are problems, such as those in genetics which we discussed, where it does not arise. However, strictly speaking it is universal applicability which is the limit attained, rather than ultimate truth.

Jeffreys' theory of probability based on degrees of rational belief takes the scientific method for granted and seeks to determine axioms from which it may be deduced. It seeks, as Jeffreys puts it, to "tidy it up". Since this view takes the scientific method for granted, it will not provide a language in which the limitations of the method can be discussed. Its statements are bound to be of the form "*If* science is able to approach the truth *then* it can do so in the following manner." The theory becomes a logical scheme incapable of making other than conditional statements about the world. It will not be able to elucidate whether science does, in fact, lead to truth. It is undoubtedly the case that many, including many philosophers, are prepared to take science at its face value. For them Jeffrey's analysis will provide all the discussion they desire. In this book we have attempted to undertake a critique of scientific reasoning, for which purpose it is not satisfactory to assume the validity of science among the premises from which we start.

The view of the scientific method as a process of falsification concentrates upon its use in the process of discovery. New facts will be discoverable in so far as the theories used in the search are falsifiable. As the theory passes its tests, however, the class of its potential falsifiers will diminish and the probability of the theory being universally true will increase. To some extent this is in line with the theory of Bayes.

With the view of scientific theories being logically constructed out of quantities that are directly observable, attention has been turned to the limitations of scientific knowledge. When constructed in this way, scientific theories are confined to statements of what is already known. Moreover, they operate at the level of directly observable phenomena and imply no ultimate explanation of any kind. As descriptions of what we may be said to know they are excellent. As tools for further discovery they fall short.

There is no one purpose which has to be served by scientific theories as a whole. Much of the controversy over the scientific method arises from the assumption that there is. One of the functions of theory is to serve as a tool for further research. Another is to constitute a description of the physical world—to be a summary, in fact, of what we have discovered. To some extent it represents a compromise between these views to regard scientific theories as descriptions by analogy. Such a view embraces the theories both as summaries of acquired knowledge and as tools for further exploration. On the other hand it envisages no ultimate explanation by the unfolding of inner truth. The cosmological problem is removed from the direct sphere of science. Scientific knowledge forms the basis on which it may be discussed but does not, by itself, provide the answers. To do this it would be necessary for science to provide reasons why its pronouncements, which are always "as if" statements (the phenomena observed to take place are the same *as if* the physical world were constituted in a certain way) should be taken as something more, reasons, that is, for passing from the simile to the metaphor. On the other hand science provides a description of the world of experience and if we are to consider possible explanations, the first thing we must do is obviously to familiarise ourselves with the situation as it exists, which we are hoping to explain. Science can do no more than hint at possible explanations; it cannot guarantee that any explanation exists. As Wittgenstein of the *Tractatus* said, "We make to ourselves pictures of facts. ... The picture represents facts in logical space." He went on to say, however, that the picture is a model of reality, it is linked with reality and that it is like a scale applied to reality. But we know nothing of a reality to which it may be linked. We familiarise ourselves with new experiences by picturing them with the help of old experiences, with the patterns of which we are already familiar. We understand our experience by relating it to a system which we know how to operate. We learn the pattern which it appears to follow.

BIBLIOGRAPHY OF SELECTED READING

An attempt has been made to grade the books. Those marked * are elementary or classical texts suitable for the philosophical section of an elementary library; those marked ** are more advanced while those marked *** are mainly mathematical or difficult reading.

AITKEN	** *Statistical Mathematics*
AYER	* *Language, Truth and Logic*
	** *The Problem of Knowledge*
BARNES	** *The Philosophical Predicament*
BERKELEY	* *Principles of Human Knowledge*
BONDI	** *Cosmology*
BRAITHWAITE	** *Scientific Explanation*
BRIDGMAN	** *The Logic of Modern Physics*
BUTTERFIELD	* *The Origin of Modern Science*
CALDIN	* *The Power and Limits of Science*
CAMPBELL	** *The Principles of Electricity*
COHEN and NAGEL	** *Introduction to Logic and Scientific Method*
CONANT	* *On Understanding Science*
CROMBIE	** *Medieval and Early Modern Science, 2 vols.*
D'ABRO	** *The Rise of the New Physics*
DAMPIER	* *A Shorter History of Science*
DURANT	* *The Story of Philosophy*
FEIGL and BRODBECK	** *Readings in the Philosophy of Science*
FISHER	*** *Statistical Methods and Scientific Inference*
	*** *Statistical Methods for Research Workers*
	*** *Genetic Theory of Natural Selection*
GARDINER	** *The Nature of Historical Explanation*
GELLNER	** *Words and Things*
HALL	** *The Scientific Revolution*
HANSON	* *Patterns of Discovery*
HARRÉ	** *Introduction to the Logic of the Sciences*
HESSE	* *Science and Human Imagination*
	** *Forces and Fields*
HEISENBERG	** *Physics and Philosophy*
HULL	* *History and Philosophy of Science*
HUME	* *Theory of Knowledge*
JEFFREYS	** *Scientific Inference*
	*** *Theory of Probability*

JEVONS   * The Principles of Science
JOHNSON-
  ABERCROMBIE   * The Anatomy of Judgment
KNEALE   *** Probability and Induction
KRONER   * Kant
LEWIS (editor)   ** Clarity is Not Enough
MACMILLAN
  (various authors)   ** The Revolution in Philosophy
MCVITTIE   ** Fact and Theory in Cosmology
NORTH HOLLAND
  PUB. CO.
  (various authors)   ** Turning Points in Physics
PAPP   *** The Philosophy of Science
PASSMORE   * A Hundred Years of Philosophy
PLATO   * Republic
PLEDGE   ** Science Since 1500
POPPER   ** The Logic of Scientific Discovery
REICHENBACH   *** The Philosophical Foundations of the Quantum
                                     Theory
                                *** Space and Time
RUSSELL   ** History of Western Philosophy
                                ** Mysticism and Logic
                                ** Human Knowledge: Its Scope and Limitations
RYLE   * Dilemmas
SCHILPP (editor)   ** The Philosophy of G. E. Moore
SCHROEDINGER   * Science and Humanism
SENDEN   ** Space and Sight
SOMERVILLE   ** Elements of Non-Euclidean Geometry
STACE   ** Theory of Knowledge and Existence
STEBBING   * Philosophy and the Physicists
                                * Logic in Practice
                                ** Modern Elementary Logic
                                *** Modern Introduction to Logic
TOULMIN and
  GOODCHILD   ** Philosophy of Science
                                * The Fabric of the Heavens
WATSON   ** On Understanding Physics
WISDOM   ** Foundations of Inference in Natural Science
WITTGENSTEIN   *** Tractatus Logico Philosophicus
                                *** Philosophical Investigations
                                *** Blue and Brown Books
WRIGHT, VON   *** Treatise on Induction and Probability

INDEX

Date Due